SUNDOWN

A Daughter's Memoir
of Alzheimer's Care

SUNDOWN

A Daughter's Memoir
of Alzheimer's Care

Judith
Harway

Branden Books, Boston

Library of Congress Cataloging-in-Publication Data

Harway, Judith.
  Sundown : A Daughter's Memoir of Alzheimer's Care / Judith
  Harway.
        pages cm

ISBN 978-0-8283-2529-5 (pbk. : alk. paper)
1. Alzheimer's disease--Patients--United States--Biography.
2. Alzheimer's disease--Patients—United
        States--Family relationships.
3. Mothers and daughters--United States--Biography.
I. Title.
RC523.2.H365 2014
616.8'310092--dc23 [B]

                    2014023653

Paperback ISBN 9780828325295
E-Book ISBN 9780828325302

Branden Books
PO Box 812093
Wellesley MA 02482
www.brandenbooks.com

For my sisters in T.S.T.

"Memory is the only way home."
    —Terry Tempest Williams

Acknowledgements

Two chapters of this book have been made into artists books and included in the following exhibitions:

Memento Mori (in collaboration with Sylvie Armstrong) –
"Jewish Artists and the Book," University of Wisconsin-Milwaukee Special Collections, September - December, 2012.
"Wandering" Harry and Rose Sampson Jewish Community Center, June - August, 2012.

To Dust You Shall Return (in collaboration with Ashley Sprecher) –
"Text/Context/Subtext," Harry and Rose Sampson Jewish Community Center, June - August, 2013.

Though I am certainly overlooking many people here, I send heartfelt thanks to all of the following: to Adolph Caso of Branden Books, for his patience and support; to the Milwaukee Institute of Art and Design for a perfectly timed sabbatical year, and to Barbara McLaughlin, David Martin, and Leslie Fedorchuk, for years of friendship and collegiality; to the Milwaukee Jewish Artists' Laboratory, particularly Jody Hirsh and Natanya Blanck, for constant incentive and a safe place to try out new ideas; to the dear, sturdy souls whose critique made this book far better than I could ever have made it on my own – Carol Sklenicka, Amy Rosa, Kathleen Dale, Louisa Loveridge-Gallas, Bill Murtagh, Rick Krause, Dan Armstrong, and Rick Ryan – and to Dana Borremans and Chloe Gribbin for making it look so good; to "Dr. Y," to the geriatric care consultant, and to the caregivers who eased my mother's passing; to the many wonderful friends who inadvertently contributed to this book by contributing so much to my life (a woefully incomplete list would include my families at Bryant's Neck and in Ireland, plus Pat Armstrong, Julie Bartos, Benedicte

Bayi, Debra Brehmer, Liz Cloud, Cecelia Condit, Graciela Fendt, Bruce Grudzinski, Darcey Rojas, Erica Schmidt, Maria Terres, and Elizabeth Vogt, along with the folks named above and below); to Curtis, a perfect companion for long road-trips, and to my other canine fellow travelers; to Maura and Richard, Alice and Hannah; to Sylvie and Keith, and to Dan – with all my love; and to my mother and father, who gave me both life and stories.

Names of institutions, caregivers, and a few other individuals have been changed.

Table of Contents

I.

II.

III.

IV.

V.

I.

"...how flimsy is the infrastructure of cognizance, where our reason, memories and identity lie. It's everything, but it's a delicate and finicky synaptic soufflé. Once it falls, nothing will make it rise again."

-- Eleanor Cooney, Death in Slow Motion

"When lilacs last in the dooryard bloom'd…"

April 2010

It is the last spring of my mother's life, although I do not know that as we drive together down Milwaukee's lakefront on a perfect afternoon. The spring sun lavishes its gold touch on the water, gilds the sweep of Bradford Beach, steeps budding trees along the bluffs in honeyed light. Because Mom always forgets to bring along her heavy, wraparound sunglasses these days, she's wearing the cheap pair I keep in my glove compartment, and still, she covers her eyes beneath both hands.

"Look, Mom," I say, pointing out at the beach, "There are so many ducks!" She nods her head vaguely. The sun is a burden to her. Though I'm driving in traffic, I know she takes pleasure in watching birds so I pull at her arm. "They're just off on the left, Mom. Look." She turns toward me, nodding again, and I realize that she is keeping her eyes firmly shut.

My mother hardly ever goes outside anymore. When I come in to visit, she tells me about all the places she wants me to take her: shopping, to the movies, back to New York just one more time, to Cape Cod, out for a fancy dinner, to visit her sister (who died 20 years ago)… A few of her wishes would be easy to grant, so I show up at least once a week with an outing in mind. "Go ahead!" my father nearly shouts at me, crazy for a few moments of respite. My mother proves all but immovable.

Today, after lots of cajoling, I manage to guide her to my car, stow her walker in back, dig out that extra pair of dark glasses, and, take her for a drive. I imagine my father closing the door behind us with a deep sigh. He cannot acknowledge his need for a break from the relentless demands of caregiving. Though I live ten blocks from my parents and they are registered with two eldercare agencies, he refuses assistance as a point of pride: *he* does not need help. Each week, if I am to give him a break, I must convince him that nothing in the world would make me happier than performing this charade once again, in which I insist that my life will be incomplete if I do not take my mother out for a drive *right now*, despite my impossibly full schedule and all of Mom's dithering protestations. He finally relents. It seldom works out well.

My mother is uncomfortable and fidgety in my car. "Where's Norman?" she asks, for the hundredth time. "He had a few things to take care of," I answer, "so let's just enjoy this drive, you and me." "Where's Norman?" "We'll go home to him in a few minutes." "Didn't Norman come with us?" By this point, it's second nature to cycle through the same meaningless patterns of conversation, and I have no idea how desperately I will repeat such empty sentences in the months to come. I have no idea how impossible it will become to take her anywhere. I have no idea what lies ahead.

Though my mother has had a diagnosis of Alzheimer's dementia for the better part of a decade, it bugs me that she keeps her eyes closed so often lately. It's a beautiful day, damn it, and I set aside these hours specifically to share it with her. She's the one, after all, who taught my sister and me to look closely, to live appreciatively. She's the one who loved naming flowers and birds, who never missed a chance to exclaim about the wonders of nature. At this moment it matters to me that she should open her eyes and engage with the world outside.

I catch sight of a stand of lilacs to the right overhanging the tennis courts. "Look, Mom," my voice is rising, "Look at the lilacs!" In truth, the lilacs are kind of ratty, but I really, really want her to open her eyes and notice something. "Look at those lilacs – they're beautiful!"

Eyes closed, Mom intones, "Beautiful. *When lilacs last in the dooryard bloom'd...* That's a poem about Lincoln's death. Do you know it?"

I'm delighted by this old, deep memory surfacing: as a girl, my mother learned many classic poems by heart and held them dear. The sound track of my own childhood memories is rich with the sweet lilt of her voice reciting Keats and Wordsworth, then rising into her favorite turn-of-the-century parlor songs as my sister and I drowsed on our pillows waiting for her goodnight kisses. How

14

much more can she recall now, I wonder? "Mom," I say, "I can't remember who wrote it. Can you?"

"Somebody or other. Maybe Robert Browning."

It's not Browning, of course, but I'm reluctant to correct her. Though her love of poetry and her gift for storytelling have a good deal to do with the fact that I am a writer and English professor today, I swallow Whitman's name. It is enough that she remembered the first line. I slowly finish the tercet as she mumbles along on this perfect afternoon:

When lilacs last in the dooryard bloom'd,
And the great star early droop'd in the western sky
  in the night,
I mourn'd, and yet shall mourn with ever-returning spring.

Apologia

When I was small, my sleep was haunted by an enormous white ox. This creature strode upright on two legs, and it would stop for nothing. As an adult, I find the details comical: the ox was always pushing a shopping cart, wearing earrings, heading straight for me. As a child, this image spiked my adrenaline.

The ox returned again and again. I came upon it in the Star Market where my sister and I tagged after Mom for Saturday grocery shopping. I met it in a garden full of exotic birds, and in an old riverside textile mill like the ones we passed every summer on the drive to Cape Cod. She (I never questioned that the ox was female) was big, strong and weirdly beautiful. And always bearing down on me without even noticing I was there.

Not surprisingly, I've talked about this dream with a therapist or two. It doesn't take a lot of insight to parse the obvious metaphor: dominant mother runs over submissive child. I bought that interpretation when I was younger and lacked a coherent life of my own. But now that I'm fifty-four years old, my children are grown and my mother is dead, I view the matter differently. My mother never set out to run over anyone: she just had places to go in her life, and she was in a hurry. She wanted to have it all, an education, a career, a beautiful home, a happy marriage, gifted children to fulfill her dreams, opportunities to travel the world. What she meant to trample was the passive model of womanhood she had been raised to embrace.

Every mother on the block wore gingham shirtwaist dresses, watched *The Edge of Night* on TV, and glued Green Stamps in their collection books. The fathers backed their Chevy Bel Airs and Ford Falcons down the driveways at eight every morning, and returned by six to sit out on their porches with a loosened tie and a beer in hand. They were young executives and small businessmen, the first generation educated on the GI Bill. The house I grew up in, a creaky old Victorian in a Catholic neighborhood of Rochester, New York, was my parents' first home together. If I had a choice, I could not have picked a sweeter place to live as a child.

I once tried to remember how many kids lived on our block: there were five in the house next door and ten across the street; two other households on the block with five kids each, plus two families with six and another with eight. When I reached forty children, I gave up. To this day, though, I can count and name all the Jews in the neighborhood. The Schwartz's, directly opposite our house, had two children, and the Weisbergers, around the corner, had three with whom we were inseparable playmates; my parents had my sister and me. Two out of three Jewish fathers were professors, and all three mothers had careers: one a lawyer, one a teacher, one a psychologist. Every other mother on the block stayed home.

In elementary school, I could not have told you that the psychology of children with mental and physical disabilities was a central preoccupation of my mother's professional life, or that she was a passionate advocate for programming that would enable all children to reach their full potential. Her career intersected with my life only on days when we had no school and tagged along with her to the United Cerebral Palsy Clinic. As Mom retired to a distant office to administer tests and design treatment plans, my sister and I explored a strange environment brimming with strange new children.

Sometimes we participated in group activities, songs and finger plays, and sometimes the teachers asked us to help out: we wrote things down for children who couldn't hold a pencil, fed kids at snack time, or moved wheelchairs from place to place. One boy named Herbie became my special friend: though his arms and legs jerked spasmodically and his speech was nearly unintelligible, his sassy attitude always made me laugh. Every time we left the classroom together, he'd crow "Step on it!" and I'd race to the end of the long linoleum corridor, pushing his wheelchair as fast as my legs could manage.

Inevitably, a teacher stepped into the hall one day as we flew past. "Herbie, stop that!" she shrieked, a misdirected scold that sent him into gales of hiccupping laughter. I jolted to a halt, nearly

17

dumping him from the chair. As she yelled at me, I glowered at her feet: I knew I had done something wrong, but I also felt wronged by her anger.

Of course, my mother received a full report. On the way home, she lectured me about being careful, about understanding the differences between people. She said that I had disappointed her. I protested that Herbie liked for me to run, to which my mother responded, "Do you think he'll like it when you tip his chair and run over him?"

I started to cry. Mom glanced at me in the rearview, pulled over and turned to face me with a serious expression. "He likes it?" she asked. I nodded, sniffling. She sighed. "Can't you just talk with him instead?"

I shook my head no, choking on my words: "Herbie never gets to run around."

My mother reached across the seat-back and touched my cheek with her right hand. It looked like she might cry, too. "What a sweet girl you are," she said; then added gently, "I don't ever want to *catch you* doing that again."

Long after I was grown, I heard my mother telling an unfamiliar story to my children: When she was only thirteen, she said, a neighbor family hired her to babysit for their son. Ronnie was a sweet, placid baby, and in the many months she cared for him she never saw him act cranky or restless. He just smiled and cooed, drifting off to sleep in her arms like a newborn even as he passed his second birthday. He also never showed any motivation to walk or to learn more than a few simple words. Around the time he turned three, his parents took their doctor's advice to place Ronnie in an institution for the rest of his life because, they said, "he belongs with his own kind."

This was the late 1930's, and my mother was told that "his own kinds" were called "Mongoloids" or "Mongolian Idiots." At the time, some "experts" claimed that these individuals represented a type of genetic "throwback" to more primitive human form. This explanation made no sense to her, but Ronnie was gone forever.

She had no choice but to swallow her grief and store the image of his little face and his crooked toothless smile in her memory.

Once my kids were in bed, Mom and I sat in the kitchen playing dominoes. "What brought that sad story to mind?" I asked. She shrugged. They apparently had asked her a question I never thought to ask: "Why do you do the work you do?"

If I had a choice, every memory of my mother would reflect the way I saw her as a child. She possessed a gift for making magic from commonplace things. When she brushed our hair before bedtime, she sang out the numbers until, after one hundred strokes, my sister and I collapsed on our pillows feeling dazed and glamorous. Our lunch boxes never contained peanut butter and jelly, which she regarded as a mark of maternal laziness: we opened our tins to find salami on rye, tuna salad sandwiches, a thermos full of macaroni and cheese or chicken noodle soup. There was always a piece of fresh fruit and a treat for dessert to remind us of her love. When I was cast as a spring flower in the second-grade play, I stepped out on stage in an extraordinary daffodil hat my mother had fashioned from crepe paper; blundering through the garden dance number, sunburst petals radiating from my head and silk ribbons tied at my chin, I felt certain that no more beautiful blossom could ever grow in our neighborhood.

I developed pneumonia shortly after my sixth birthday. It was August, and late summer sun lit the western sky with banners of orange and purple each evening as all the kids on the block came out to play one last round of Capture the Flag or Red Rover in the street. The doctor's orders for me – three weeks of bed rest – felt like a life sentence. I was to get up only to use the bathroom. Day and night, the laughter of my playmates tormented me, blowing in on the breeze through my open bedroom windows.

Each morning, my mother helped me up, helped me wash and dress, then arranged a nest of pillows for me in the bed she shared with my father. I settled in to read comic books and watch game shows on TV, while Dad left for the office and Mom busied herself in the kitchen or at her desk. During the school year, this might

19

have been an agreeable arrangement, but it burned me to see my sister board the day-camp bus each morning with a sack lunch and her swim-bag. It's a mystery how my compromised lungs survived the crazy tantrums I threw that summer.

My sister's birthday fell towards the end of my convalescence, and Mom had planned a party. Birthday parties at our house were legend among the neighbors: my sister and I took for granted that a dozen or so children would join us in a yard festooned with streamers, that our cakes would be iced with pink or purple frosting. For one party, our mother drew a bashful donkey on a length of butcher paper, then taught the guests how to braid five strands of plastic boondoggle into colorful tails we blindly pinned as close as we could manage to the poor beast's bald rump. For another, she showed us how to make party hats from overturned paper plates decorated with flowers, bows, and ribbons that tied beneath our chins.

Though we are almost two years apart in age, my sister was only one year ahead of me in school. She was slight and willowy, a wisp of a girl; by contrast, I was tall for my age, not to mention broad-shouldered and boisterous. She was quietly precocious and I was a bit of a ham. Still, we took pleasure in dressing identically and being mistaken for twins. I adored my sister, and never left her side. My envy of her was constant and complex.

And so, despite my lethargy, it was intolerable for me to imagine her at the center of a dazzling birthday party while my quarantine continued. I begged my parents, to let me come downstairs, shedding tears and lying about how well I felt. If it had been up to my father, I might have won, but Mom stood firm.

The morning of my sister's birthday, I woke in a funk of self-pity. Soon, however, surprising things began to happen. A favorite baby-sitter showed up, and as she decorated the kitchen with balloons and streamers, my mother brought a stepladder upstairs and decorated my room just as cheerily. Moments before the guests arrived, Mom placed a pink construction paper crown on my head and a Dixie cup full of jellybeans and gumdrops in my hand to sweeten my mood as the sound of excited voices began to rise from downstairs. Just when the laughter and music of party games became too much to bear, the door of my bedroom opened and there was my mother, carrying a tiny cake adorned with a ring of sugar flowers and a single candle burning at its center. "Happy un-birthday to you," she sang, as she set the tray in my lap, and I silently made a wish, the same anxious wish that rose in my heart whenever I glimpsed the evening star or tugged at a wishbone, that my family and I would be safe and happy forever.

When the cake was gone, Mom blew up two long, twisty blue balloons and challenged me to a duel. Though her rules required each swordfighter to remain seated and move only within a restricted radius, cries of "en garde!" and "touché!" soon left me breathless and coughing. It was time for a quieter game. "One, two, three," she counted, and each of us tossed our balloon to the other, watching them corkscrew in lazy arcs through the space between my bed and her chair. After so many days of whining and insisting that I was ready to get out of bed, I suddenly found it pleasant to rest my head on the pillows as my mother retrieved the balloons from the floor again and again, bending and rising to toss an awkward arrow gently back to me.

At last she rubbed both balloons on my hair, generating enough static to stick them to the wall. My sister appeared in the doorway, wearing her pink dotted-Swiss dress and a crepe paper tiara, her face smeared from ear to ear with chocolate frosting. It was time for Mom to return to the party. But in that moment, I saw something unfamiliar and strange in my sister's eyes: a twinge of jealousy. Though she was the birthday girl with a dozen guests and a big pile of presents, for a little while, I'd had the best of our mother completely to myself.

Since my mother's death, I dream fast and furiously, as though trying to pack a lifetime's worth of rapid eye movement into each night of sleep. In one dream I enter a bare, cold room to find my mother huddled on the floor in a pile of raggedy old blankets. I kneel beside her, take her in my arms. She is chilly to the touch and smaller than life. "Am I alive or dead?" she asks. I hesitate;

21

then choke out, "Dead?" like a question. She nods soberly: "I thought as much."

I leave her, hoping to find help, but the world outside has no connection to that prison in which my mother lies. An elegant couple passes. "Don't you recognize me?" the man asks. I do not. He introduces himself as a boy whose heart I had broken at the age of sixteen. In real life, I never apologized to that boy, but in the dream I tell him that I still feel sorry for being unkind, that I never meant to be a source of pain or sorrow in the world.

The dream shifts, my mother fades, and eventually so does the boy who had not crossed my mind in decades. I breathe with such peace I am reluctant to break the spell by waking: one small overdue apology draws me and my mother closer to forgiveness for all the important things we left unsaid.

Oxymoron: The Progress of Dementia

I first became aware of my parents' curiosity about retirement communities more than a decade before they actually made the move. At that time, Mom and Dad still lived in the big brick house in Pittsburgh where my sister and I had spent our adolescence. Besides the fact that the house was built into the side of a hill, making its three stories interact with the landscape as four, it faced a cobblestone street so steep that cars could not drive up it on icy days. Rather, one had to pursue a circuitous route on more heavily traveled roads, then turn at the top of the hill and skid down to our address. It was not a convenient home for an elderly couple, particularly as Mom's eyesight and mobility diminished.

Little by little, my parents found their social circle shrinking. A few friends died, and others moved away to be closer to children and grandchildren. My parents flirted with the idea of moving south, gathering brochures from seniors' communities in North Carolina. When my husband and I moved from Milwaukee to the Chicago suburbs in 1995, we suddenly had my parents' attention: despite the combination of terrible weather and ridiculously high cost of living, Chicago was on their intellectual and cultural radar. At Dad's behest, I dutifully visited every retirement residence within reach of our home, but it was easy to see why they did not feel ready to make such a move. Healthy and barely seventy, they settled instead upon a beautiful lakefront condo, where they remained for the next ten years.

For a time they attended every soccer game and music night at their grandchildren's elementary school, enjoyed their book group, came over for dinner two or three times a week. Then circumstances changed for my husband and me, and we relocated back to Milwaukee. My father announced that they would move along with us, but by then my parents had friends, interests, and many reasons to stay in the Chicago area. They were still mobile, and we reassured them that we were only moving ninety minutes north. Weekly visits became the routine.

Looking back, I'm pretty sure that I misread the early signs of Alzheimer's, and found it hard to be patient with my mother. She and I had enrolled together in a drawing course at a suburban arts center, the type of class she had often taken in her youth and in which she expected a lot from herself; for my part, I had always intended to take such a class but had no expectations. In the first few weeks, my drawings of random objects (a jacket slouching off a coat-hanger, a can of Coke, a philodendron) garnered praise in our amateur moments of critique, while my mother struggled over drawings that could have been executed by a talented sixth grader. Her clumsy efforts and her overt jealousy mystified me.

One day I stepped out of class to move the car and happened to meet a neighbor; we fell into conversation, and when I returned to the studio twenty minutes later, I found my mother in a state of panic. "How could I know that you were ever coming back?" she screamed, "How could I know you weren't dead?" Then she loudly told the teacher that the whole damn course was stupid. I apologized to everyone and coaxed her out of that classroom. We never went back.

After my husband and I returned to Milwaukee, Mom's speech and behavior patterns became more repetitious. She often seemed disorganized, but I chalked it up to the fact that she was just getting old. Daily tasks like cooking dinner overwhelmed her, yet my father's protective attentions kept her largely oblivious to the changes she was experiencing. She trusted his cheerful explanations of why they were eating out every single night ("We worked hard for years, and now we have the money to enjoy this"), participating less frequently in activities they enjoyed ("Nobody in that book group reads the book anyway"), or ceasing to travel ("The airlines pack you in like sardines these days").

My father has never been comfortable discussing personal information, so I was not privy to details of the diagnosis. What I know is that it came not from a specialist but from my parents' general practitioner, and for reasons I will never understand, neither he nor Dad saw any point in consulting with a neurologist or a geriatrician. My father, ever the protective husband, assiduously shielded Mom from the A-word through the remainder of her life. Once the general practitioner had labeled her confusion and forgetfulness "early Alzheimer's" and prescribed a low dose of Aricept and Namenda, my parents plowed forward. Years later, as Mom moved into a nursing home, I was to learn that the diagnosis, the medication, and the dosage had never been revisited or reconsidered: once the diagnosis had been made and an initial approach to treatment established, that was that.

My father presented this diagnosis to my sister and me by handing each of us a typed half-sheet of paper transcribing the substance of what Dr. X had said and reminding us that this was confidential information, never to be shared with our mother. He described a few of her symptoms to us in whispers, as if we hadn't noticed them already, hissing, "There's nothing we can do in the long run." This was the only acknowledgement of her condition that he would allow. The discussion remained closed for most of the following decade.

I give my father great credit for slowing the progress of Mom's cognitive deterioration. His domestic sorcery concealed the growing extent of dysfunction from her view, and sometimes from ours as well. On a daily basis, they continued to cope, but when any little thread was pulled, the whole fabric of their lives came dangerously close to unraveling. Once my father spent a few days in the hospital following surgery, and my mother woke alone in the night calling out for her Mama and Pop, unaware that she herself was a grandmother. When my father felt faint and I took him to the emergency room, my mother was so overwrought that she fell and hit her head as we were leaving: she was carried back in as a patient to the same ER, to be cared for by the same doctor who had admitted her husband to the hospital a few hours before. She didn't recognize him, didn't remember that we'd spent the day there with Dad. After asking the same question about a dozen times, she yelled at the doctor, "Young man, I have always had a perfect memory."

As Mom's confusion and erratic behavior began to have a limiting impact on my parents' lives, we tried to persuade them that it was time to accept a little more support. I did months of research on their behalf, knowing that they had expressed interest in the amenities of a retirement community that offered a continuum of care (increasing care and services should an elderly resident become ill or disabled) on the premises. Every time it looked like something might fall into place, my father balked, telling me that I was over-reacting to minor symptoms or announcing that he would rather buy a house because he and my mother needed privacy.

At last, after four years of vacillating, my parents purchased a beautiful apartment in a lakefront retirement facility in Milwaukee and arranged for renovations that would suit them. The timing seemed perfect to my husband and me: my father had faced a couple of significant health scares, and my mother, increasingly confused and dependent, could not be left alone for more than an hour or two.

As soon as the deal was done, however, Dad panicked. I began receiving distress calls from the sales manager at the seniors' residence: when my parents attended meetings about the renovation of their apartment, my gentle, quiet father grew angry and belligerent, my mother dissolved in tears. My father had signed his name to terms he was not prepared to honor, wanting to own the apartment as insurance but refusing to move into it. When I visited the place with my parents, Dad would pace through the spacious rooms fuming about how tiny and cramped they were, then look out over the spectacular view of Lake Michigan and the downtown skyline, muttering, "This place reeks with the stench of death." Eventually, he reneged on the whole deal. I still can't stand to think of how much money he threw away.

Mom's journal from this time reflects her growing confusion and impairment. The entries are brief, repetitive, and childlike, and each asks essentially the same thing: why had they come to this "Bad Patch" (her capitalization) in their lives? A few entries mention specific examples of my father's increasing depression and anxiety: that he had yelled at a nice lady in Milwaukee, presumably a representative of the retirement community; that he had put money down on a new car, then canceled the check as soon as they got home. I only remember my mother confiding in me once during this period: "I don't know what to do," she said, "because I've never had problems before. Other people have problems and I try to help them, but I have never had a single problem in my life."

After another year had passed, Dad could no longer pretend that he was able to care for Mom in their condo; he again started looking into retirement communities in Milwaukee, though he had burned his bridges with that first one. He settled on Umbria Court, a complex that was being expanded and renovated in a good location on Milwaukee's east side, very close to our home. Even so, with a lovely apartment selected and all the paperwork signed, my father panicked at the last minute and announced that he would move into the Jewish home instead. This made me laugh – on our first go-round, when I had tried to get Dad to visit there because I thought he would feel more at home among neighbors with the same background as his, he had grumbled, "I don't want to live with a bunch of crabby old Jews." Suddenly he insisted that we take a day to visit, just to keep his options open.

This visit proved unforgettable for me, though I am quite sure that neither of my parents retained the memory of it. As a sales representative led us through the lobby, an elevator door opened and a team of EMTs came rushing out, wheeling a gurney upon which lay a man who appeared to be dead. Clearly, this was a terrible mistake: there are protocols, after all, for moving a body discreetly, instead of just blasting through the main lobby in full view of everyone. My mother screamed and burst into tears. My father still insisted on visiting several apartments before we could get out of there.

I like to think that I'm a supportive person, but I did not relish handling the details of my parents' transition to a seniors' residence. I had my own growing family, my own career to attend to. And my father is not a man who suffers assistance from others graciously. In the months preceding their move I repeatedly drove to the Chicago suburbs to help sort through their belongings; each time, my father assured me that no aid was needed, refusing to allow me to look inside closets or drawers. When the movers showed up, they had no choice but to pack and move exactly what they found. Helping my parents unpack into a much smaller apartment I opened box after box full of garbage: junk mail going back five years; random slips of paper off my father's desk; folded paper bags, packaging from various purchases, gallon bags of twist-ties or the plastic rings off milk bottles. There were four large boxes full of empty jars, carefully wrapped in paper for the move. There were, in short, countless clear and concrete reminders of how much I had chosen not to see.

My father also brought with him a raft of bad decisions: they would not entertain in this new apartment; they would not make any friends; they would not participate in any activities sponsored within the building. Some of these strictures loosened with time, and others didn't. My mother, who was by far the more social partner in their marriage, would have enjoyed meeting others in the building and participating in the book groups, attending the concerts. By the time they moved, however, she had declined enough that making friends was difficult because each meeting was the first, and my father's depression cued her to react badly to the overtures of neighbors.

The move meant that Mom and Dad would be living just ten blocks away from my family and me. After unpacking (I covertly removed as much of the detritus as I could), they settled into a new routine and once again my father cajoled everyone into believing in the appearance of normalcy. The degree to which Mom was struggling only became visible when daily life threw her a curve. When the elevator was out of order on a day I came to take her shopping, she hammered on the door with her cane and got into a shouting match with the workman who unwisely hollered up the shaft "You think that's gonna help?" All my efforts to redirect her failed. She stood there in the corridor yelling and cursing like a longshoreman, until it finally occurred to me to appeal to an older aspect of her identity: "Mom, I don't feel well. I need to get to a bathroom." And suddenly, she was guiding me back down the hall to her apartment, happy to be caring for a child.

Because my father could never admit his need for a break from caregiving, it wasn't easy to get both my parents out for anything other than necessary errands or lunch. I'd invite them to a movie matinee, order tickets, and then find myself getting cross at Dad for reneging at the very last second, shoving Mom into my car as she loudly complained, "Your father never wants to go out with me these days." Every time I tried to schedule an outing to provide him respite, he balked and resisted: he didn't need *respite*, he insisted, pronouncing the word as though it were obscene. So I continued to dutifully buy movie tickets for both of them, knowing full well that he'd ditch on me when I came to pick them up.

My mother loved to go to the movies, in her mind. Until her last days, she cherished memories of Saturday double features with her childhood friend Mabel. These memories account for why I always bought the tickets online: she was alarmed by the fact that a movie cost more than a quarter. One day she decided to buy the popcorn because I had bought the tickets: "This is highway robbery," she snapped at a startled teenage concession clerk. And it wasn't easy to find a movie that fit the bill: anything that disturbed her even slightly could set off a firestorm. Upset by scenes of child abuse at the start of *The Secret Life of Bees*, she attempted to incite the whole audience to rebellion. I struggled to guide my nearly blind mother and her walker out of a darkened theater, step by painfully slow step, as she shouted at those who remained, "This is a terrible film! Everyone decent should hate it! What kind of people are you anyway?"

In the summer of 2009, my father lost his driver's license after causing an accident which, but for the miracle of side airbags, might have killed my mother. The degree of his own debility was laid painfully bare during the days that followed, as he placed the scene of the accident fifteen miles away and in a different county from where it had actually occurred. When I managed to track down the details and obtain a copy of the accident report, he alleged that the cops had falsified the location. Every time he spoke about the crash the narrative changed, and with each re-telling he seemed to be wrestling to get the story under control. To my sister and me, it was clear that Dad had been lost and seriously disoriented at the time of the accident; it frightened us that he was not able to internalize the fact that he was at fault, that two cars were totaled, that the other driver had been injured, that there had been a five year old child in the other car... I still don't understand how he escaped a lawsuit. My sister and I pressed my father's doctor to revoke his license pending review, one of the hardest things I have ever had to do. As we expected, Dad could never sort out the paperwork to reapply, though to his dying day he insisted he was going to get a new license.

The loss of driving privileges marked a shift in the balance of caregiving responsibilities. Dad could still hold on for the daily household routine, but my sister and I gradually took over payment of his bills and arrangements for transportation and services from an eldercare agency. His study had long been a muskeg of random papers, catalogs, bills, magazines, and notes to himself, none of which he would permit us to sort through or throw away. As for assistance, he was willing to accept only a single three-hour shift every week, during which he and my mother would go to the supermarket and drug store. Other than that, he refused to leave the building unless my husband or I came for them.

The eldercare agency and the skilled nursing unit attached to Umbria Court, Cascia Hall, played significant roles in Mom's last couple of years, as Dad was forced to accept help with transportation and, eventually, with care for his wife. A proud and private man, my father's determination to cope alone and his abhorrence of the idea of in-home care were to shape many of the most difficult decisions our family had to make as Mom's dementia progressed. My father's love/hate relationship with retirement living had come full circle: the life that he and his wife had shared grew steadily narrower, leaving him no choice but to grudgingly avail himself of services he once imagined to be attractive in a seniors' community.

Mom's detachment from the appropriate manifested itself in other ways besides griping about prices and stomping out of movies. Though she raised her children with great sensitivity to others, she grew disarmingly honest about voicing whatever popped into her head in old age. Annoyed by a sullen sales clerk, Mom would not even lower her voice as she pronounced, "These Chinese women are always rude." At a birthday dinner, something reminded her of a limerick which she promptly repeated several times:

The poor benighted Hindoo
He does the best he can do –
He sticks to his caste
From first to last,
And for trousers he makes his skin do.

I regret that this rhyme will stick in the minds of her grandchildren forever. At the same time, I'm not sure this lack of self-censorship is such a bad thing in the end. In any case, after a lifetime of probity and propriety, this is generally what we are left with. Society demands that we edit ourselves and create self-aware personas as we develop, and this carries over into much of childrearing... until, by random chance, we draw the wildcard of Alzheimer's. If it is true to say that my kind and accepting mother was not herself at the end of her life, it is equally true that she became a totally unedited version of herself. Which of us, honestly, does not stereotype, or recall a thoughtless schoolyard rhyme from childhood?

I am not embracing hateful words here, but seeking to contextualize them. When I came home from grade school chanting a racist jump-rope rhyme, innocent of its meaning, my mother sat me down and asked me how I would feel if someone said things like that about my family. When my mother, at the end of her life, chanted ugly rhymes she learned in childhood, I had no choice but to put my arms around her and tell her, once again, how much I loved her.

31

Sins of Memory

May 2008

While staying in a cottage in the Smokey Mountains, I happen to pick up a book called *The Seven Sins of Memory*, by Daniel Schacter. Schacter's purpose, to develop a comprehensive taxonomy of memory faults, is far ranging and ambitious. He examines the brain mechanisms of memory distortion that account for seven ways ("sins") that memory can fail us. Though the book is not specifically about Alzheimer's and I am a thousand miles from my parents, I read every page in terms of my mother's dementia.

Reading and writing on the porch of that tin-roofed cabin, where the silence of my thoughts is crowded by birdsong all day and the trilling of frogs through the night, I am grateful to feel so far away from home. It still is possible for me to leave my parents, knowing that my husband will look in on them once or twice a week. My father is able to care for my mother's basic needs by maintaining a rigid daily routine that manages her erratic moods and keeps her on track: she cannot neglect to get out of bed in the morning because he guides her through the steps of rising and dressing; she cannot forget to eat because breakfast is set before her in exactly the same way every day. She still can go down to the common room for an occasional activity because my father walks her down and back to ensure she does not get lost. They take dinner in the dining room, always at five-fifteen. I take for granted all the ways in which my father keeps the house of cards in which he and my mother dwell from collapsing.

Though I wear many hats at home – wife, parent, daughter, teacher, colleague, caregiver, and neighbor – I have come to the mountains to take off all but one: here, for a few blessed weeks, I am only a writer. I have come to work on a project that has nothing to do with caring for my parents, or with my mother's decline. I have come to get lost in my imagination and find my way into new poems.

But then I come upon that damn book about memory faults. My mother is with me, always…

The Seven Sins of Memory
(*after Dr. Daniel Schacter, PhD.*)

"Memory…can be a troublemaker."

I. Transience

What town is this we're in?
my mother barks across
the beige formica table of a diner
five blocks south of her apartment.
We're in Milwaukee, Mom.
She looks around the room,
intent as if she's following a road
that winds away beyond dim headlights.
Have I been here before?

*Yes, Mom, I answer, we eat here
at Ma Fischer's every week.*
Shaking her head, she sighs
and says, *Sometimes I think
my memory isn't all it used to be.*

II. Absent-mindedness

Lost keys. Lost glasses. Lost
prescriptions. Lost eye drops.
Missed appointments. Unpaid
bills. Small losses

33

make a maze of daily life.

Leaning on her cane unsteadily
my mother says, *I love to tap dance*
(present tense) *and I'm good at it, too.*
And of a close friend, dead ten years,
she says, *We tell each other everything.*
Over lunch at the seniors' residence
she takes off her dark glasses,
rests her hand on mine, confides
that sometimes she forgets
she has a body: *It just goes away,*
she says, and then I feel
the way I felt when I was eighteen.

That's my daughter's age.
She's new-moon slim, shy,
absolutely conscious of the body.
Her dancing is nothing like
my mother's buck and wing, but when
I overhear her with her friends I know
they tell each other everything
(and I mean *everything*).
And though I tire of fighting
my way back up the sharp slope
of my mother's memory dropping
to a past I'm less and less a part of,
how I love, for just a moment,
seeing her misplace those years.

III. Blocking

Riding in the car with her four grandchildren
my mother beams. The conversation's quick
as water falling, never mind the jokes

34

elude her. My son, behind the wheel,
takes a bump too fast and Grandma
shrieks. His sister teases
with a rhyme from childhood:
Five little monkeys bouncin' on the bed,
One fell off and bumped its head...

One went airborne and bumped her head,
a cousin sings back. My mother sits
among these grown-up children
wanting still to teach them nursery poems
and songs, to comfort them
at bedtime. She says: I know
the real version. It goes:

Three little babies bouncin' on the bed
Two were sick and the other was dead...

The kids fall silent. In the catch
of smothered laughter, they don't dare
meet one another's eyes for fear
that bouncing dead baby
will set them giggling. Finally,
the youngest cousin speaks:
That's cool, Grandma!
And my mother beams,
bouncing home with her babies.

IV. Suggestibility

After leafing through old photographs
all afternoon, my mother catches
her reflection in a mirror. Her hands
fly to her hair. My God, she cries,
I'm starting to go grey!

Her hair's been grey more than
two decades, but the lovely girl

she was, posed in an arbor,
had her jet-black hair pinned up
with an antique ivory comb.
Her dress was taffeta, a rose
pinned at the waist. My mother
pats her hair, turns from the mirror.

Lucky for me, she says, *I take after
my mother*, meaning my grandmother,
whose hair was bone white all the years
I knew her. *She had thick dark hair
like mine, with just a dash of white
for drama later on.*

V. Bias

When my son was twelve
he caught his grandma cheating
at a board game, and he challenged her.
All afternoon he sulked
up in his room, until my daughter
told me, *Mom, he's got a right
to be upset.*
           My mother spent
her whole adult life helping
unloved children, speaking to them
kindly. She taught us
*If you can't say something nice,
don't say anything at all.*
But now she comments loudly
in the grocery store, the bank,
the theater: *That fat guy's belly*

is disgusting, or *That woman*
has the biggest chest I've ever seen.

Impulse bleeds to speech
like a red sock in white wash.
So she gave her grandson
what she has left to give:
You've always been
a goddamned pain in the ass.

VI. Misattribution

Shortly before we heard
the diagnosis, Mother started writing
stories for her grandchildren
so they would come to know
the many faces that she'd worn,
the people that she loved. She wrote

about the brand new Model T
her father won in a church raffle,
about racing pigeons cooped
up on the roof, her dancing classes,
summers at the beach. She wrote
achingly of boys who went to war
and never came back, of the year
she finally left home, the telegram
she sent to recommend herself
for graduate school, the quiet
classmate she married
as they earned their PhDs.
But history slipped from her grasp
as she composed it, as she came to write
about her children as she knew us,
stories my own children read

37

with hunger, this one, for example:

The year I turned thirteen
a riot broke out at my school,
black kids and white kids fought
with sticks and bottles right there
in the halls. I was so scared
I panicked, froze. But luckily
an older girl took charge of me.
She brought me to her house,
she called my mother, who rushed home
from work to comfort me....

The wonder of this story is
it never happened. None of it:
No race riot. No fighting.
No blind terror. No big girl
who took me in. No mother
rushing home to rescue me.

But I loved that story,
my daughter tells me,
and I answer, *Go ahead and love it.*
Just know it's hers, not mine.

VII. Persistence

Ten years old, my mother stands
(in her mind) at the top of a wind-blown
New Jersey hill, the rolling buttercups
and Queen Anne's lace tickling her shins.
At her side, her cousin Rog,
more of a brother, really, one year older,
squint-eyed, sun burnt, ready
for whatever this day brings:

for riding milk-cows, daring
younger siblings to touch
the new electric fence, damming
the creek, sitting quiet in the shade.

Her uncle's farm, her paradise,
was a prison farm for women.
His wife left him in the thirties
when she learned
he had a taste for younger prisoners.
But these are the best days
of my mother's life, the dazzling
sun swept days of childhood she revisits
every time a smell, a sound, a name,
a voice remembered wakes the past,
the present disappears like magic
right before her eyes.

I read somewhere that Alzheimer's,
the cruelest disease, is crueler still
to those who suffered most
in childhood. My heart breaks
to see my mother locked inside
her memory. But Holocaust survivors
her age spend their waning years
confined behind barbed wire,
starving and aching for their parents,
drawing death into their lungs
with every breath. For my young mother,
running barefoot down a sloping field
of daisies, I give thanks.

What Makes a Reuben "A Reuben?"

May 2010

It becomes harder and harder to take my parents out. My mother puts on a game face, but there are few places we can go without courting disaster. My father is growing so reclusive that I'm giving up on him. The only outings I can count on to be successful are meals at familiar restaurants where everybody knows what bad shape we're in, but today I have taken Mom to a diner we've never eaten at before. I read somewhere that this place has the best Reuben sandwich in Milwaukee, and lately Mom wants to eat nothing but Reuben sandwiches.

As usual, my mother asks for her husband every few minutes. "Where's Norman? When is Norman coming back? Why isn't Norman here?" She is voluble and bright, however, and reminiscing aloud about VE Day. It does not dampen her spirits when an old man at the next table lapses into unconsciousness, and his wife and his nurse both begin to shout, "Julius? Julius? Julius?"

On VE Day, my mother tells me, she took the subway to Times Square with her best friend Mabel and Mabel's father, because *this was history.* Mabel's father insisted on holding both girls by the hand so as not to lose them in the crowd. Having seen pictures of my mother and Mabel together – the former a slender and striking brunette, the latter slightly plumper, with cascading blonde hair and enormous eyes – I suspect that he was not simply concerned about losing them in a crowd: these girls were head-turning beauties.

At the neighboring table the wife and the nurse keep shouting: "Julius? Julius?" Incredible as it seems, the restaurant's owner, an overbearing Russian émigré, leaves his daughter to attend to this calamity and saunters over to take our order. He seems to disapprove of my desire for a turkey sandwich: I should really try the Reuben, he insists. Under any other circumstances, I wouldn't budge, but my mother is enjoying both the proprietor's attention and her own reminiscences. As the old guy at the next table turns blue, I change my order. The Reuben.

The owner walks away, and Mom happily repeats the narrative about VE Day. I press her for details, and she repeats it once again. Finally, an ambulance careens onto the sidewalk outside, and four burly, tattooed young firefighters burst through the door. They remind me of the paramedics who picked up my mother the previous Fourth of July when she fell and hit her head in the Umbria Court dining room. And of the crew who helped when she passed out in her apartment. And of the EMTs that arrived when she tumbled down the stairs of my house on Christmas Eve five years before. And of the cops who rushed to our rescue when she did a nosedive outside Evanston Hospital seven years ago, right after her husband was admitted... I have the deepest respect for EMTs. But still Mom doesn't register the hubbub around us.

Suddenly, something catches her eye. "Judy," she stage whispers, "I think there's a problem here."

"Yes, Mom. There's a guy over there who needs help."

The paramedics crowd in a tight circle around Julius, who refuses all attempts to take him to the hospital. Julius, I cannot help overhearing, is ninety-three years old. His wife is worried sick. The nurse seems unable to stop shouting. But Mom's interest in the drama quickly wanes. "Do you like that sandwich, Mom?" I ask, and she answers with a stock line: "The Reuben is a New York sandwich. I haven't had a good Reuben in ages." Never mind the fact that Mom orders a Reuben every time we have lunch together.

Over my mother's shoulder, I can see Julius gasping for breath, as his wife's voice rises in a whine of anxiety and the nurse keeps scolding. Against this crazy backdrop, the restaurant owner comes back to ask us, "Is everything OK with your lunch?" I am struck by how calmly he engages Mom in a discussion of the finer points of what makes a Reuben "A Reuben." She is thoroughly charmed.

41

He turns away, heading back to the kitchen. Mom glances around the room and notes, for the first time (in her mind), the scene with Julius and the EMTs.

"Jesus Christ, Judy!" she shouts in alarm, "The cops are raiding this joint!"

Living to Tell the Tale

As an undergrad at the University of Michigan, I was moved to tears in a Shakespeare lecture when the professor himself began to cry while walking the students through what must have been his 500th reading of *Hamlet*. A short, balding, middle-aged man, Professor R paced back and forth at the front of the lecture hall, waving a copy of the play in one hand though he seemed able to recite the whole text from memory. He was parsing out the scene where Polonius delivers a load of tendentious advice to Laertes, when suddenly there was a catch in his voice:

This above all: To thine own self be true,
For it must follow as dost the night the day,
Thou canst not then be false to any man.

"To thine own self be true," he repeated, *"To thine own self be true."* Though now, as a middle aged English professor myself, I know the connection to be rather conventional, that lecture was the first time I learned that Shakespeare's phrasing echoes the Oracle of Delphi who tried to give poor old Oedipus the heads up about the need to "know thyself." And this is where the lecture really got under my skin. *"Know thyself,"* the professor intoned. "What would it take to truly *know* one's self? Can a person bear to be fully honest? Can a person look so deep inside that he spares himself nothing? Can anyone ever see clearly enough to truly *know thyself?"* Some of his words I remember, and some I am reconstructing from memory. I will never forget the tears on his cheeks as he faced the class and said (this is verbatim, I'm sure), "Perhaps this is the most profound injunction in all of literature. Perhaps it is impossible."

Have I embellished this memory over the years? Probably. Despite decades of teaching English, I had to look up the exact wording of the quote from *Hamlet*. If you asked the student sitting next to me in that class in autumn 1975, he or she, I don't

43

remember which, may recall the whole scene differently, if at all. Because this is what I remember, it is my truth, and in that small measure *to my own self I am true.*

What makes each of us who we are? Genetics? History? Biochemistry? Temperament? The peculiar accident of being born in a particular place, at a particular moment, to particular parents sets in motion a cascade of random chance and serendipity that shapes individual identity: of all people in the world, in all of history, I am myself, I inhabit this body in this time and this place. In her famous poem "In the Waiting Room," Elizabeth Bishop writes about the moment a child begins to realize the particularity of identity and the bonds that hold us to others:

> *What similarities*
> *boots, hands, the family voice*
> *I felt in my throat....*
> *held us all together*
> *or made us all just one?*
> *How – I didn't know any*
> *word for it – how 'unlikely'...*
>
> *How had I come to be here...*

One reason why I find this poem a pleasure to discuss with students is that most feel a familiar resonance with that tiny revelatory instant, with a child's dawning awareness that there is a self to be known, and that self depends upon a web of human connections. But even when, at the age of twelve, I first came upon the poem in an anthology, long before I could claim any understanding of it, I associated it with my mother. Bishop's portrayal of the child in the waiting room matched the way I imagined my mother as a little girl: precocious and complicated beyond her years, brimming with questions in a family where children were to be seen and not heard. Even the detail of paging through the National Geographic matched up: as a child, my mother spent whole afternoons exploring the world through National Geographic photographs, a memory she shared with me for the first time when I was small enough to be cuddled in her lap, peppering her with questions about the strangely painted people dancing through the magazine. We are separate and we are one.

As my older child was first learning to talk, she struggled to grasp the concept of pronouns. When my husband and I spoke to her, we called her "you," and so, in her mind, that designation became hers and hers alone. Likewise, we each referred to ourselves as "I," which seemed to her to be a word for people other than herself. Thus, in an anxious moment, she would toddle over to one of us, reach her arms up, and say, "I pick you up?"

Needless to say, this reversal caused some trying moments. When another child in the playgroup grabbed a toy from her, she would shout, "That's yours!" And as that child ran off with the contested toy, my daughter would cry, "You want that!" The fact that the other mothers laughed at these backwards exchanges only increased her distress. One of those mothers even snatched a toy out of her hands, and when my daughter howled, "That's yours!" the mother held the toy high up in the air and responded pertly, "Thank you. Now it's mine." We didn't last long in that playgroup.

Even at the time, my husband and I understood that our child's confusion made sense. She was extremely verbal, and her early access to speech gave us glimpses of her complex inner life at an age when many people still think of children as simple, impulse-driven beings. To understand pronouns, she had to understand identity as something both fluid and fixed, she had to master the rudiments of point-of-view: she defined herself by how we addressed her; she had yet to establish an internal sense of "me."

As an aside, our daughter's early speech also spawned some remarkable metaphors. Shortly after her brother's birth, I overheard her playing with a small plastic seesaw. "This is big sister, and this is baby," she said, positioning a tiny person on the seat at either end. Then she placed a slightly larger person in the middle, exactly at the fulcrum: "And this is Mommy." She was barely two years old.

If my children could recall their infancies, I wonder if they would look back and say, "It sure was hard work to be a baby in this family." They were loved almost to excess, doted upon, nurtured, read to, coddled... and ambushed at every turn by the familial presumption that they would be extraordinary. I don't recall my own infancy, of course, but from this distance I can reflect upon all the things I did as a young mother that must have mirrored my own mother's attentive care and high expectations for her very young children. My daughter, a cuddly cherubic baby with Shirley Temple curls, quickly became her grandmother's favorite. My mother, the teller of family tales, delighted in narrating this precocious baby's development, embellishing moments beyond the recognition of even her proud parents. Thus, Mom's stories had my daughter shouting, "Quack, quack, quack!" at a flock of ducks when she was barely eight months old, a "memory" that fails to jibe with what I saw at exactly the same moment.

My daughter's pronoun confusion rankled my mother. She seemed to regard it as a flaw that we should "correct," but my husband and I saw it as a transient quirk, a bit of "kid logic" that would right itself eventually. As first time parents, we were far too anxious about most things, but in this instance we got it right. For once, we didn't over-instruct: we just used pronouns as a natural part of speech and trusted the English language to work its magic on our child.

Sure enough, within a matter of weeks, our daughter began to call herself "I" and the rest of us "you." The process of learning was so natural as to be almost imperceptible. My parents, who lived 500 miles away at the time, heard her proclaiming ownership of toys by saying "That's yours!" at one visit, and "That's mine!" at the next.

Once upon a time I faulted my mother for what I saw as her insistence on controlling the family narrative. OK – in truth, that's not just once, and the time spanned decades, from adolescence into my forties. Mom had a gregarious nature and a passion for storytelling, and (though she would have denied this vehemently) she never let the truth get in the way of a good tale. I resented being a character in her hands.

My parents were both clinical psychologists, which means that their careers were dedicated to other people's stories. My father, erudite and shy, quickly found his niche in academia; my mother stayed in the gritty trenches of lived human experience throughout her long career. The dinner table conversations we heard growing up were cornucopias of vivid tales. My sister and I would chatter on about school or friends, but in the center ring there was always the larger-than-life spectacle of what my mother had heard that day, which patient's story brought her to tears, how she was moving heaven and earth to help some poor soul. The heartbreaking tales she carried back from the office contrasted starkly with the dominant upbeat narrative of home. To hear her tell it, ours was a perfect family: she was a beautiful and successful professional woman married to a handsome and successful professional man; their children, angelic and gifted, were the best daughters in the world. I had a very fortunate childhood, but "perfect" is a word I've never trusted: if our family was perfect, why did I so often feel unhappy?

When I was small, I struggled to recognize the border between my imagination and real life – assuming, that is, such a border existed. I would go so far as to say that I heard voices – or perhaps, more accurately, I heard one narrator's voice, which told the story of my life as I lived it. The endless stream of language coursing through my mind impelled action as much as describing it. "She walked across the street in dappled sunshine," my interior voice declaimed, as I crossed from curb to curb beneath the elms. It was as though the act of telling was what made me real. Once in a while I would slip up, as when my mother handed me two milk-of-magnesia tablets and I heard myself saying, "But I can't stand these lousy things, *she said.*"

"What's that?" Mom asked. Chastened, I repeated the complaint without the attribution.

Entering adolescence, my own narcissism muddied the family waters. It grew harder and harder for me to bear not being the star attraction at the dinner table. My mother was working with tormented teens, coming home with lamentable stories of alienation, anorexia, suicide attempts. I was getting up every morning and heading off to a high school I hated; I was skipping classes, smoking pot, chasing after boys who had nothing to recommend them but a driver's license, living on coffee and chewing gum day after day... What did my mother know of me, I wondered. How could she not see *my* alienation, *my* depression, *my* desperation?

Needless to say, whenever she or my father expressed their concerns I shouted them down. I pushed them away. Meaning to be respectful of me, not a common concept for parents of their generation, they took a big step back. I took this as a cue to plunge forward, heeding the drama of my inner narration, and sometimes I think I'm lucky I survived.

In time, my interior narrator matured, and storytelling itself saved my life. If I could tell compelling stories, I didn't have to be so hell-bent on taking crazy risks in the name of living them. If I could write, I could experience anything. If I was afraid, I could narrate courage on the order of my favorite song from *The King and I*: I whistled a happy tune until I started believing I was OK. And, soon enough, I was OK. I passed through the best educational channels, learned how to find meaning through work, married a wonderful man, came to rest in a tranquil home. And with every step I came closer to forgiving: If it was my mother's role to control the family narrative, didn't it make sense for her to tell a story in which we all could be happier than we actually were? Wouldn't my interior narrator want to do the same?

Some years later, when my daughter must have been around ten years old, I overheard my mother telling her a story about her early pronoun confusion. In this story, however, rather than gradual

48

acquisition of the concept of pronouns, there was a turning point when so much was at stake that my daughter could not risk being misunderstood. As my mother told it, we were walking down the street near my parents' house in Pittsburgh when a neighbor stepped out to meet the grandchild. My daughter was sitting in the stroller speaking of herself in the second person the way she customarily did. This neighbor, intending to be nice, remarked, "What a beautiful baby!" and my daughter replied, "*I* not a baby. *I* a big girl."

Well, *I* was there, and *I* am certain that my mother's version of the scene is largely fabricated. The neighbor, a famously bossy guy, was the butt of many stories in my family that actually did happen, but this isn't one of them: when he came out to admire my mother's beautiful grandchild that day, said grandchild fussed because her stroller had stopped mid-walk, though she couldn't have cared less what the grown-ups were talking about. I don't remember exactly where this meeting with the neighbor fell on the timeline of my daughter's mixed-up pronouns, but they are entirely separate narratives in the catalog of my mind.

This story became one of my mother's stock favorites for telling at family get-togethers. I chafed every time I heard her tell it because it seemed to me to function as a way to control the identity of the favored grandchild. It's not that Mom's version reflected poorly on my daughter; I resented that the story added to the pantheon of myths that gave my mother dominion over what role each of us played in the family narrative. (My sensitivity to this matter stems from the fact that well into adulthood I was generally cast as an over-emotional drama queen who could not take care of herself. Every time I received any kind of recognition – from a degree, to a proposal of marriage, to a job offer, to a major grant – family congratulations were tinged with surprise.) To be fair, I cannot know what my mother actually remembered. Did she conflate different elements – my daughter's confused pronouns, her own concerns about the next generation of our family being perfect, her annoyance at this neighbor calling her brilliant grandchild a "baby"? Was the scene she narrated real to her? If it was real to her, doesn't it rise out of her memory? Setting aside the old axe I was grinding for years, who am I to say her memory is false?

I'm not talking about dementia here, but about the relativity and particularity of remembering. Without memory, what is identity? We define ourselves by what we have experienced, where we have lived, who we belong to. Our stories give us our names, our culture, our family. Our stories are who we are.

After my mother retired and continuing until she was stricken with Alzheimer's, she wrote many stories and poems for her grandchildren. From 1993 through 2003, every Hanukkah brought another volume of "Stories from Grandma" – clumsily typed, illustrated with line drawings and blurry Xeroxed photos, spiral bound at Kinko's with a different bird sticker on the cover of each copy, chosen for each grandchild. It was the sweetest gift in the world. I felt a twinge of guilt that it sometimes irritated me to read aloud her version of history at bedtime.

I was also slow to internalize what Mom may have been telling her grandchildren about her own identity with each quirky quarto: had she, too, been the kid who heard an inner narration, who needed to tell the story of her life even as she lived it? Had her need to master narrative been similar to the impulse that made me write?

This was my mother's gift to the future: a chance to glimpse her internal sense of "me," to experience her memory. But memory ineluctably tangles with memory loss in this narrative. In some of Mom's later stories you can see what may be the smudgy fingerprints of early dementia: broken sentences, poor spelling and structure. Stories that make little sense to her daughters, although we are featured prominently in them. She kept writing until she no longer could.

Most diseases ravage the body, but Alzheimer's ravages the identity. A person with Alzheimer's loses her life the way someone might lose the keys that unlock their home, or lose a treasured heirloom that simply vanishes during a move. Losing memories means losing the things that make us who we are: our experiences, our friends, our children. In the end, a person can continue to live after having, in many senses, already lost her life.

If I could write the definitive story of my mother's life, I would compose it of happy memories and to hell with veracity. For a period of years, due to her optimistic nature, dementia allowed her the grace of nostalgia as she cycled back through earlier and earlier times, as her perfect grandchildren blurred into her perfect children who, in turn, blurred into her perfect childhood. It wasn't until I had to face the reality of losing her that I began to cherish all of her stories, no matter how skewed and confabulated. By the time memory failed her so completely that the sugar-coated past melted into nightmare, I had finally learned to listen. And forgive.

Karma

As a young woman, my mother wore pearls even when she walked us to the playground. She was a dark haired, dark eyed beauty, and although she took the greatest pride in her intellectual and professional accomplishments, she also loved to tell my sister and me about the summer she worked for Germaine Monteil cosmetics in Manhattan: when she chanced to meet Madame Monteil in the elevator on her way back from lunch, Madame told her, "You could be a model for me. You just need to lose twenty pounds." Mom didn't have twenty pounds to lose, and she had enough good sense to say so.

Before my sister and I were born, a photographer friend of my parents shot some portraits of Mom. She looks serious and sexy in these pictures, lips closed to conceal the overbite that was her only visible flaw. Her hair is drawn up in a French knot, the gown is slipping from her shoulders, and she gazes into a mirror as if no one is watching her. These are portraits of seduction and mystery.

Growing up, I never saw my mother as pretty in the present tense. She was simply a fact of my life. She dressed better than most of my classmates' mothers in elementary school because she went to work every day while the neighbor women stayed home vacuuming and cooking. She wore her long hair pinned up in a ridiculously intricate bun, two swirls held in place on top of her head by countless bobby pins, an elaborate, center-parted wave at the front. Now and then, one of my friends commented upon my mother's dramatic looks, but as a pre-teen I already tended to respond to pictures from her younger days by saying, "Wow, Mom – you *were* beautiful."

As I struggled to grow into my maturing body, I pulled away from identification with my mother. She gained a lot of weight after giving up smoking, and everything about her was hopelessly out of date. I cringed as I watched her struggling into her girdle, slipping on her stockings and clipping them at the thigh, hoisting her heavy breasts into a heavy bra, pulling a lacy slip over her head, then concealing the whole show with a polyester knit dress that

52

suited her professional image. I went to school in mini-dresses I'd cut from Indian bedspreads and sewn by hand; I wore jeans I never washed; I paired shoulder-length gloves from the thrift shop with a bulky flannel shirt. I knew for sure that my mother had no sense of style whatsoever.

Mom remained on the heavy side through middle age, as I began to make it my business to shed more pounds than anyone ever should. With hindsight, I now see the pattern of eating disorders as a hallmark of my mother's family: my grandmother was hospitalized as a young woman because, as she told me once, "I stopped eating altogether. I simply didn't feel like it." My mother's sister was slim and pretty until, three children into a miserable marriage, she exploded into obesity; by the time she died, her husband was perversely fond of saying that it took four men to carry her body out of her house. I never gave my mother credit for aging with grace because her evolution from glamour girl to pleasant looking matron coincided with my own dawning determination to control and "perfect" the hand that nature dealt me.

I never appreciated the fact that I looked like my mother. I wanted to look exotic, natural, cool, unique, and beautiful in my own right. But I always looked like a clumsy, lighter-haired, updated version of her. The spring before I was married, when we were at odds over nearly everything, I showed her a picture of myself on the top deck of the Staten Island Ferry, windblown and laughing: at the very moment she said, "You look exactly like me," I said, "Jeez, I look so ugly here!"

So many things I wish I could un-say.

As the first of my mother's daughters to marry, I was blindsided by the baggage she brought to the planning. Everything about her own wedding had been horrible in the eyes of her parents: she was marrying *a Jew*, for goodness sakes, so she had to have a judge officiate instead of the parish priest. The groom's mother had a foreign accent and little education. And she, the bride, planned to have *a career*.

53

I cherish the few photographs that were taken at my parents' wedding, though they look nothing like the proper church wedding Mom had been raised to anticipate – my mother in a grey wool suit on the right, flanked by her parents with their queasy expressions; my father, also in a grey wool suit, on the left, flanked by his mother, who is managing a brave smile (he was marrying *a Catholic*, for goodness sakes), and her brother Charlie, who probably had to be pried away from the racetrack to escort her. The only judge they could engage came from traffic court, and he showed up drunk. One of the few wedding guests had appeared before him to challenge a ticket that very morning.

Keeping up the appearances my mother had been denied was definitely not in my wedding plans. Her thwarted dream of the formal white gown, the big crowd, the music and flowers, the traditions and unbridled celebration, collided with what I wanted, which was mostly just to do things my own way. Formal gown? It had to be Mexican cotton. Big crowd? Only people I knew and loved. Tradition? Forget it, my husband-to-be and I were writing the script for ourselves. Though we clashed over every detail, my insistence on independence in the planning was something my mother modeled for me very directly.

It's possible that this same dynamic was at play when my first child was born. I'm sure it's not unusual for a young mother to feel the need to hold her mom at arm's length, or to want time to get to know her baby on her own. But unlike most, I felt empowered to assert that my husband and I needed space and time, and asked my parents to wait two weeks before visiting. My mother was angry and hurt. As ever, we clashed because we were too much alike.

Now that I have raised two children to young adulthood, I don't know how she survived raising my sister and me. Or, rather, I finally do know how she survived: she did her best, which is what mothers have been doing since time immemorial, even as her daughters failed to appreciate her and said things they could never un-say. To us, she was never a beauty or a role model: she was simply our mother. And mothers, as my children have often reminded me, can be awfully annoying. One more glance from the immutable face of Karma.

Mom used to tease us that no matter how rotten we kids could look, we cleaned up OK. I didn't notice that she was losing her ability to clean up OK until she and Dad arrived in Milwaukee. I wonder, from this vantage, how bad things had gotten before he agreed to the move: Mom had stopped cooking, stopped driving, stopped writing, stopped using the telephone. Still, it seems to me that in rather short order after they landed at Umbria Court, Mom stopped washing her hair or changing her clothes. As Alzheimer's reduced her sense of self-consciousness before others, I clung to glimpses of her former self: the lipstick smeared roughly on her mouth as they prepared to go down to dinner, the silver necklace she wore because she still could manage its simple clasp.

Little by little, my mother grew outright slovenly. Stained shirts, unwashed hair, un-brushed teeth, smelly underwear… surely my father noticed, but he held his head up high for the both of them. Inevitably, his carefully constructed routines were breaking down. He could no longer get Mom up in the morning, and because she was lying in bed so long, and at such unpredictable hours, she began to soil herself.

This turn of events was beyond his ability to cope. I remember him calling me one morning in August 2010 as I was leaving for work: the fact that he asked for help at all told me that he was desperate. He could not get her up, he said, though she was lying in a dirty bed, and she would not let him bathe her. I rushed over, roused Mom, got her into the shower ("Do you want to wash your own bottom, or do you want me to do it?" "You do it."), and changed the sheets before going on to my office. My father, expressing awe at how much I was able to accomplish and how quickly, insisted that the soiled bedding go into the trash instead of letting me wash it. My mother seemed completely oblivious to the morning's drama. Despite our concerted efforts, my father and I had reached a point where we could not count on making her

55

presentable. The point where he began to think about moving her to Cascia Hall.

As my mother's decline accelerated, I began to reflect upon how many of my passions in life trace back to her: though I did not inherit my mother's gifts for needlework and design, she gave me my love of reading, my appreciation of nature, my need to nurture, my delight in cooking. Because my husband and I belong to a Community Supported Agriculture co-op, the regular delivery of opulent local crops rekindled an interest in pickling and preserving that goes back to my mother's brandied peaches, which I loved to help prepare but steadfastly refused to eat. And her pepper jelly. And her green tomato relish.

Though I had dabbled in pickles and jams, the act of canning became an obsession in the summer of 2010. Mom's need for a higher level of care loomed inevitably before us. How could I resist the comfort of preserving sweet, wholesome food for the winter? The farm provided peaches: I canned peaches, made jam, experimented with chutney. The farm gave us blueberries and cherries: more canning, more jams. Tomatoes, peppers, zucchinis: four varieties of tomato sauce, plus three varieties of salsa. Cucumbers, cabbages, onions: sweet pickles, dill pickles, four kinds of relish.

As the summer ripened, my kitchen grew so prolific that my husband placed a six foot tall bookcase at the base of the cellar stairs, and I packed it with three rows of jars per shelf, double decker. My sister and friends joked about "shopping" at my house, or teased me about my survivalist tendencies. I couldn't slow down because I couldn't resist the scented steam filling the kitchen on a hot July night; the jam or sauce slopping onto the nice clothes I had worn to teach summer school, to visit my parents, to rush them to appointments; the improbable blessing of waking up next morning to a dozen jars cooling on the counter, with their vivid colors, textures, tastes. The jars reassured me, as I rose from my troubled sleep, with their promise that nurturance was tangible and real.

"You need a logo," my husband said, when it was clear that my therapeutic obsession had gone way beyond anything our household could hope to consume. I chose for my mascot the beautiful mug of my dog Boo, who came to us years ago as a one-eyed stray with a tragic back-story and a truly great heart. I adapted my favorite photo of her to a homemade label, and "Boodle's Best" products rolled off my stovetop and out of my kitchen, between days of eldercare and nights of insomnia.

Near the end of her life, Mom could sometimes talk about canning. I'd tell her what I was putting by, and she would follow her own threads of thought back into a monologue about vegetables her father grew in his victory garden in empty lots around their house in Flushing. Even on days when she didn't recognize me as her daughter, she could list the produce her parents preserved in the thirties; if I was really lucky the reminiscence of canning green beans would allow me to coax a bite or two past her lips when eating no longer seemed necessary to her.

If the fact that I coped with a share of my grief through cooking can be laid at my mother's doorstep, so, too, can the presence of my mascot Boo in my life, along with other sad-eyed strays who have shared my home over the years. Mom could be quite critical of her own children – we had, after all, enjoyed every advantage in life, including, she would hasten to point out, completely enlightened mothering, so we had no grounds for complaint – but she uncritically took all manner of lost and hopeless souls to her heart in the years I was growing up, both through her work as a child psychologist and through spontaneous acts of heartfelt generosity. An old transient who helped her turn over the garden every spring always got a good dinner along with his pay; a ragged handyman went home wearing an old tweed jacket of my father's. She fed stray cats, encouraged us to bring home garter snakes and crayfish as pets (which did not, in retrospect, have any need to be *brought home*), and counseled youths with anorexia or suicidal impulses without seeming to notice that her younger daughter was doing her level best to disappear from the face of the earth.

I'm writing this on a muggy night in July 2011. It's over ninety-five degrees. My mother has been dead for seven months. Dear old Boo, grizzled and gimpy, dogs my heels as I move from room to room around the house. It pains me to think that this will likely be her last summer of life.

On my stove, black beans, strawberry jam, and tomato sauce boil down in their individual pots, steam rising into the humid air of the kitchen. My nose must be glowing red the way my mother's did every summer after she reached a certain age, when her undiagnosed rosacea began to take its toll. My own rosacea was diagnosed ten years ago, and is fairly manageable when I pay attention to the doctor's instructions; I do not face a certain sentence of ruddy complexion and broken veins in my nose as my mother did in her dotage. But, like her, I passionately continue to do all the wrong things: to dig in the garden without protection of a hat, to cook over a hot stove, to burn my candle at both ends and keep a drink at my right hand, to work too damned hard and to beat myself up about things I cannot possibly accomplish.

Because he loved my mother for over six decades, I have no way of knowing what image of her my father preferred to hold in his mind at the end of her life, or what face he imagined this evening when he asked me to print up a few of my favorite pictures for him. My selections favor the young woman who wore pearls to the playground, though I'm throwing in a few choice shots of the matriarch with grandkids. There's a paucity of photos of her from the age that I am now, what we call "middle age," although that suggests a lifespan of well over a century. Such euphemisms have greater appeal to me now that the lighter-haired, updated version of my mother that I face in the mirror relies on hair-dye to conceal the grey. Like my beautiful mother before me, I'm trying to keep up appearances. But the truth is, I don't clean up as good as I used to.

Incompetence

By autumn of 2010 there was no dodging the fact that my father could no longer care for my mother on his own. He was so dedicated to her and had grown so meticulous (read: compulsive) about her care, that he could not stand the thought of her being alone for even a moment; at the same time, with his self-conscious and intensely private nature, he couldn't stand the idea of hiring in-home help. Mom needed the support of a professional caregiver long before she moved into the nursing home, but Dad held on until he absolutely couldn't manage. Even when she stopped getting out of bed, stopped eating and stopped bathing, he still blocked the door when the social worker from Cascia Hall came to visit at my request. "My wife is dressing," he said, denying any troubles, though the social worker could see her lying flat on her back in the other room, could hear her shouting, "I'm freezing! Bring me a goddamn blanket!" When pressed, my father would agree to increased care (and I don't mean a big increase – I mean an increase from one to three three-hour shifts per week), then the minute I walked away he would cancel everything.

I now understand that Dad's vision of moving Mom to the nursing home relied upon his belief that he could continue to tend to her twenty-four hours a day. He had so fully come to define himself by his role as her caregiver that he couldn't imagine any other structure for his life. And yet, when we proposed the option of the two of them moving together into assisted living, where she would receive needed support but wouldn't have to go all the way to the nursing home right away, he refused: she was to go to the skilled nursing unit because she was ill; he would stay where he was because he was perfectly fine. Then, because he couldn't trust anyone else, he would supervise her care every waking minute.

In order to move my mother to Cascia Hall, a move that she would never have accepted had she been conscious of it, we had to activate power of attorney for her healthcare. And in order to legally activate POA, we had to have my mother declared *incompetent* by at least two doctors who determined that she was incapable of making decisions for herself.

In a *de facto* sense, my mother had long been a marginal voice in matters relating to her care. Since the earliest signs of her dementia, my father (with as much input from my sister and me as we could manage) had been in charge. She passively swallowed whatever pills he handed her, never questioning what they were for. When a major decision needed to be made – when, for instance, an overly aggressive gastroenterologist recommended surgery to remove a polyp when there was no evidence that it was cancerous – my father and I posed questions and discussed the case thoroughly with medical personnel right in front of her, as she sat oblivious in the corner, interrupting only occasionally to ask, "Is this guy some kind of a doctor?" or, "When can we have lunch?"

My parents' general practitioner in Milwaukee, Dr. Y, was a kind, decent, intelligent man with the regrettable habit of smiling broadly whenever he discussed a poor prognosis. The worse the news, the bigger his grin, a mannerism that would wear pretty thin during the final weeks of my mother's life. Still he approached his elderly patients with forbearance and respect. Despite threats to the contrary, my father had not changed doctors after his driver's license had been suspended by Dr. Y at the urging of me and my sister. When we informed him that we wanted to officially activate the healthcare POA for Mom, Dr. Y invited us to meet with one of his colleagues to get the second signature.

I knew what to expect. There is an inherent ugliness to the standard process of assessing cognitive decline: the doctor firing simplistic, irritating questions at the patient, repeating the questions in mixed up order to see if the patient recognizes them, the feeling of vicarious humiliation as the patient, my parent, fails again and again to produce coherent responses. As I sat waiting with my mother and father in a small examining room, chatting about Mom's commute by subway in the early '40s to one job or another, my sense of dread increased.

In walked Dr. Y's colleague, a tall, angular man with a shaven head and a pronounced German accent. He was the kind of person who talks across the elderly, addressing me as though my parents weren't really in the room. When he spoke to them directly, his voice became loud and slow, as if old age necessarily equaled stupidity and deafness. "Hello, Vivian," he boomed with false good cheer, towering over my mother, "I just want to ask you a few questions."

I could have reeled off his questions before he ever spoke: *What month is it?* "April," my mother replied. It was September. I stared at my hands, feeling protective of my mother in the face of his condescension and guilty that I wanted her to fail so we could get this over with. *Where are we?* "In a train station," Mom said, and as the doctor reached to sign the paper I regretted encouraging those reminiscences about Grand Central. *Who is the president?* Mom faltered. "Look at that," she said falling back on her rich store of social grace, "I can't think of his name. Norman, do I like this one or not?"

The same old questions: she could not remember hearing them asked several times by her doctor, by the geriatric psychiatrist we consulted when considering the advisability of that polyp surgery, by the social worker on the nursing care unit that would be her last home. They never varied, those stupid questions, and they never offered the dementia patient any sort of context. My mother, having lost the present to Alzheimer's, had no idea what was at stake in this inane conversation. But if that doctor had asked her at a good moment, she could have educated him about the history of the City University system in New York, particularly Queens College, where she was a straight-A student and president of her sorority, or about the development of Clinical Psychology, the field in which she earned her PhD. As a backdrop to these accomplishments, she could have filled him in on the history of women's suffrage, telling him the story of how her mother was thrilled to vote for the first time shortly before her oldest daughter was born. She could have reminisced about meeting the skinny, Jewish veteran who would become my father. She could have told my all-time-favorite story about why she ditched Catholicism (the last time she went to confession and confided in the priest that she was dating my father, he warned, "The university is a Godless place"). She could have evoked the sound of Paul Robeson singing in a Greenwich Village basement in the early fifties. I like to think that she could still have described my birth to him.

But that doctor was content to receive the answers he wanted. Not three minutes after meeting my mother for the first time, his signature on the form pronounced her "incompetent," and he bustled off self-importantly to his next appointment. "Was that guy a doctor?" Mom asked, and I mumbled yes. He had done exactly what I had asked him to do.

Needless to say, nursing home care is not predicated upon a spouse or family member being present around the clock. In much the same way as it is helpful to step back and let a young person adapt to life at camp or college, there is something to be said for not hovering when a loved one with dementia enters a nursing home. Everyone we talked with – the social worker, the head of nursing, the geriatric care consultant, Dr. Y himself – urged my father to limit his visits to Mom in the early days because his presence could be a stressor. We were told to expect a period of adjustment before she settled in and became comfortable with the routines of care, meals, and activities; during this time, Dad was to visit early in the day and not return. This was a tough sell for my father: he was constantly finding fault with the care Mom received because every detail, from administering eye drops to setting up the CPAP machine at night, was not handled exactly *his* way (CPAP stands for constant positive airway pressure – Mom's sleep apnea was certainly the least of her problems by then). The staff was very cooperative and helpful; my father, bless his heart, was not.

Mom did pretty well at Cascia Hall in those first three weeks. Often she seemed unaware of the transition – or she noticed her environment but didn't mind the change. So many things she didn't seem to mind: where she was, who the people were around her, how little she remembered of her life. The staff would get her up in the morning, dress and feed her and sometimes get her to engage in an activity. Dad would come over at eleven or so and stay until around two. I'd arrive at one or two and stay until four. Sometimes she recognized us and sometimes she didn't. Sometimes her detachment seemed like a blessing. If Dad did not come back, the evenings were reportedly OK; if Dad came back, and he did so obsessively, the evenings were torture for both of them.

"How is your mother?" people asked.

What could I say? For months before the move, my father remained convinced that neighbors wouldn't notice their distress if he simply avoided them. He sequestered my mother inside their apartment, setting foot outside only if I succeeded in bringing my parents to our house for dinner. Dad went downstairs once a day to check the mail and pick up a meal from the dining room in styrofoam containers.

"How is your mother?"

The rumor mill in a retirement community can be pretty active, but there was also genuine concern. My parents had some very good neighbors. My father told no one when Mom was moved, and when asked point blank he made it sound like she temporarily needed nursing care and would be home soon enough. At his urging, I sneaked in Mom's clothes and bedding; I furnished her room without being noticed.

"How is your mother?"

I gave everyone the same answer: "She's holding her own." Whether or not this was true I had no way of knowing. We had timed the move appropriately for the progress of her dementia, in that Mom was fairly content in the moment without asking obvious questions (*Why are you leaving me here? How did so many of my belongings get here?*). We could do nothing but hope that she would settle in peacefully.

"How is your mother?"

She had lost some weight, but she was OK physically. Sometimes she was happy to see me, and sometimes she had no idea who I was. Sometimes she sparkled with wit and curiosity; sometimes there was nothing but terror in her eyes.

This is how we limped through the autumn.

Whistling Past the Graveyard

Though I like to call myself a non-linear thinker, much of what I understand of the world depends upon lines. Time, for instance, implies a linear structure: sunrise always comes before noon, which leads into an afternoon that declines to sunset. Nightfall anticipates tomorrow's dawn. And human life implies a linear structure: we are born, we grow up, we procreate, we age, and we die. If we're lucky, our children live on, our posterity.

Storytelling, too, relies upon linear form: first this happens, then that happens, which causes something else to happen, and the result is where the story ends. We learn something by following the line to its logical conclusion.

Alzheimer's defies linearity. It separates past from future. The present, devoid of context, is reduced to a jumble of unrelated moments. There is no progress, none of the comforts of recursion. Just this moment. And this one. And this one. Some moments are happy, and some are sad. And if they are all identical, no one will be the wiser. Now is all you have. And now. And now.

My father in law used to tell this story from his days as a small town grammar school principal in British Columbia: he was required to read a Bible passage during announcements each morning and, finding this tiresome, he decided to test his theory that no one listened anyway. He selected an innocuous verse and read the same Bible passage every day. It took two weeks before a teacher asked him, "Wasn't that the same reading as yesterday?"

Conversations with my mother had a numbing repetitiveness for years, but I kept on trying to listen. With Alzheimer's, the saying goes, you have to listen to the emotion not the words. I called it a good day if I was able to make her laugh. We had some good days, even after the move to Cascia Hall.

"Hey, Mom," I'd say, settling into a chair beside her, "I've got a joke for you." She'd brighten. "What are you if your nose runs and your feet smell?" I've known this riddle since third or fourth grade, and she was probably the one who told it to me in the first place.

"I don't know. What?"

"You're built upside down!"

She'd chuckle contentedly. "Ah, there's nothing like a good joke," she'd say. "And that was nothing like a good joke," I'd rejoin, quoting one of our favorite scenes from Mary Poppins.

Silence for a few minutes. Then Mom would speak: "I haven't heard a good joke in ages."

"Well here's one you might like. What are you if your nose runs and your feet smell?"

She'd smile. "I don't know, what?"

Most anyone who has cared for a loved one with dementia can tell you that there are moments when the awful misfiring of the human brain can be pretty darn funny. Even in the darkest days of Mom's hospitalization, my laughter rose from some deep well of surprise when I tried to sing with her and she snapped, "Shut up! I can't sing with you people creeping around in my song." It's an unsettling sort of laughter that echoes the hilarity of hearing someone talk in their sleep: when you listen in on the unconscious in a completely unguarded moment, you can't be certain whether or not there is some deeper sense in this nonsense.

My mother was an extremely articulate person. She took pride in being unbeatable at any game that involved trivia, history, or language. Over the years she lived with Alzheimer's she narrated the chaos inside her head as if reporting live from a disjointed dream. The punch lines became so numerous that I lost track of them, but no one who was there will ever forget the time a waiter served up the lasagna she'd ordered and she squealed with delight: "It looks like something died on my plate, and it's bleeding all over the place!"

Towards the end of life Mom would cycle through the same questions a hundred times a day *—What is this place? Why am I here?* – and I would repeat the same answers. And each time the conversation was completely new, both because of her lack of short-term memory and because of her verbal inventiveness. Thus a hundred repetitions would suddenly be enlivened by an exchange like this one:

Mom: What is this place?
Me: It's a hospital.
Mom: Don't lie to me. This is a dump. It's rank! It's vile! It's a big bunch of... bananas! (I coughed to stifle a laugh.) *And you sound perfectly terrible to me.*

Or,

Mom: What am I doing here?
Me: You fell and bumped your head.
Mom: You're lying! I've never bumped anything in my life. You just want to get my mother all flipped over!

True to cliché, we laugh to keep from crying. What else can anyone do? Though she was a serious and purposeful person, my mother also had a great sense of humor. Would she have begrudged us the healthy option of whistling and laughing past the graveyard?

My best friend from high school has a unique perspective on dementia that informs my own. She is the oldest child of parents who married very young, so by the time they retired my own parents were well into their seventies. Her parents celebrated retirement with a bicycle trip through France, during which her father suffered a cataclysmic accident. Although it's a miracle that doctors were able to restore his facial features, they had less luck with cognitive function: after weeks in a coma and years of rehabilitation, he recovered well enough to function much like someone suffering from moderate dementia.

Here's a story she told me a decade after her father's accident:

Among other things, the trauma to her father's brain caused an increasing loss of impulse control. No matter where he was, if he felt the slightest pressure in his bladder, he simply unzipped his trousers and urinated on whatever was beside him. Having accompanied her parents on errands in a small Virginia town not far from their farm, she lost track of her father briefly and then spotted him down the street behind a tree. A policeman approached: "Excuse me, Ma'am. You need to be careful. We have reports of a pervert around here today." My old friend, a gifted actress and comedian, affected a southern accent and didn't miss a beat: "Why that's no pervert, Officer – that's my Daddy!"

Outside

I need to be outside. A kind of restless energy drives me, keeps me from sitting down and focusing if I have to stay indoors all day. This is not a desirable trait for a writer: I fight to sit still at my desk. I'm always jumping up and pacing, rearranging something or another, tearing out the back door and digging in the garden. A friend of mine jokes that her husband, a passionate fixer-upper, is like a little rat: if you don't keep an eye on him he starts chewing a hole in the house, poking around in wires and insulation, then filling it in and starting another hole. That's the kind of restlessness I feel when I try to sit down, still my mind, and work.

This is one of the reasons why it suits me to live with dogs. I'm not the kind of person who goes to a gym or worries about looking fit: I just like to wander around in fresh air, poke about in the dirt. Dogs need to go out every day and they enjoy the world wholeheartedly, regardless of what kind of wind is blowing or what kind of precipitation is falling. The act of walking is completely central to their lives. Where we humans walk a straight line down a path or sidewalk, they circle and veer, follow their impulses and their noses. They have no agenda but to discover what is there for the discovering.

Although my mother was not like me in this regard, I trace my need for contact with nature back to her. As a child, she helped her father tend a massive garden in the undeveloped land around their house in Queens, lots left vacant by the Depression. Instead of the thriving suburban community in which her parents intended to raise their children, she roamed a strange semi-urban wilderness of empty fields and foundations begun and abandoned. Then, every summer, she spent a month with her cousins who lived on a farm in New Jersey. I grew up dazzled by stories about those summers: she and her cousins ran wild in a world where almost nothing was off-limits. Her Aunt Florence approached childrearing as though her four boys were a rugged form of livestock, to be turned out in the morning and called back in at feeding time. The fields, the barns, the woods, the big hill behind the house with the water tank at the top, provided a backdrop to my mother's happiest memories.

Later, I would come to understand that my mother spent her summers at the New Jersey State Correctional Facility for Women, also known as Clinton Farms. Her Uncle Willie was superintendent of agricultural operations (this was a remarkably progressive model of rehabilitation developed by Edna Mahan, a pioneering prison reformer), and her Aunt Florence raised a family under pretty challenging conditions. Once the fifth child, the only daughter, came along, the two bedroom house was "expanded" to include a "hall bedroom" – meaning that they put a bed for the daughter out in the hall – but it still lacked indoor plumbing. Whatever help Aunt Florence had with the household came from young prisoners whom she took on as "projects" and sought to reform through unpaid domestic service. As my mother entered adolescence, she became friendly with some of the girls who were not very far from her age and who craved a chance to page through her movie magazines. One girl had killed her parents; my mother said this was because they would not let her go to a dance, but even as a child I knew that there must be much more to the story than that. Another, Aunt Florence told her, had been "found in a house that wasn't very nice."

Beyond a few snapshots of her with her adored cousin Rog, I don't have as many pictures of my mother's summers in New Jersey as I would like. Those I do have are pretty heavy on the dogs: Uncle Willie bred wire-haired terriers and Irish setters to supplement his income from the farm, and apparently this was a major attraction for my young mother. One picture I blew up and framed to decorate her room at Cascia Hall featured Mom at about twelve or thirteen years of age, seated among wildflowers, with her arm around her favorite terrier, Betsy. She is an impish, gangly girl with short bobbed hair. Betsy is posing like a movie star. You can see the breeze ruffling the long grass around them. Soon after the camera caught this idyllic scene, Uncle Willie lost his job and Aunt Florence divorced him because the truth came out about his relationships with some of the prisoners.

70

My mother's life took an urban turn at this point, though she retained a passionate interest in natural sciences. When my sister and I came long, she made a point of passing on to us her love of living things. She kept a garden, growing and canning peaches and tomatoes; she cooked up the fish that Dad taught us to catch; she encouraged us to care for pets, and she took pride in her ability to identify birds, trees, and flowers. Later in life, when her eyesight and memory failed, she would point at a bed of daffodils and say, "These are just like the buttercups around my father's garden," or gesture at a seagull and exclaim, "This is the same kind of hawk that used to hunt in the fields around Clinton." Sweet intrusions of deep memories into the present.

I was in college when my mother's father moved to the old soldiers' home. I don't remember many particulars, but I know that it was summer and I was staying on Cape Cod with my parents. Because I did not see my grandparents regularly, Grandpa's Alzheimer's was a bit abstract to me. One of the few overt signs of his dementia I can recall was a comment he made at a fiftieth anniversary dinner for Grandma and him: I hugged him tight, kissed him, and said, "I love you"; as I walked away I heard him ask, "Who was that pretty young lady?"

In those days, the word in common usage was "senility," and I think I regarded it as a normal part of aging that Grandpa didn't recognize me. He was over eighty after all, and hard of hearing: wasn't this just the way old people got? So I was shocked to hear that my gentle grandfather who had a degree in engineering had "fueled up" the car with the garden hose and then walked back into the house and smacked his wife in the face.

My mother flew down to Florida to help get him settled into a nearby VA Hospital. The way I remember it, she was only gone for a few days. When she returned, I was waiting on the tarmac to meet her as she walked down the stairs from the plane, a quaint greeting still possible in those days. She looked exhausted and close to tears, and when I went to hug her she pushed past me more roughly than I think she meant to. "It's really lousy getting old," she muttered, stomping into the terminal.

I only visited my grandfather once at the veterans' home. Grandma dropped me at the door and I must have stayed about an hour, pushing his wheelchair up and down corridors lined with rows of other wheelchairs, each one occupied by somebody's grandfather. Some of the old men were dozing, others trembling or shouting or drooling down their shirtfronts, and I couldn't think of much to say beyond repeating my own name and whose daughter I was. At last I wheeled Grandpa back to the room he shared with two other old men and sat down on the edge of his bed facing him. I took his hands in mine, wondering how on earth to say goodbye. As I hesitated, he looked me straight in the eye and said the one clear thing he'd said all afternoon: "I'm never getting out of this place."

Fast forward to October, 2010 and my mother's move into nursing home care: We were told that she should not leave for the first few weeks, until she had fully adjusted to the new environment. Then we would be able to take her for outings or to my house for dinner again. Combine this expert advice with my father's natural conservatism, and we expected not to take her out for a good long while. Not like she had been going out much anyway: between the loss of Dad's driver's license and the decline of Mom's behavior, they were lucky just to get down to the dining room for dinner. More recently, Mom had started refusing to leave the apartment to come to our house. This jibed with my father's increasingly agoraphobic tendencies.

Though Mom's adjustment was eerily smooth at first, she was a skeptic at heart: the part of her personality that allowed her to question the Holy Roman church in her youth kicked in after a week or so, and she began to defy anyone she saw as an authority figure. If an aide came in to wake her and coax her to dress, or to remind her that it was time to go to bed, she stubbornly refused to cooperate. She insisted that the blinds be kept closed. She declined to eat at mealtimes, demanding food when the kitchen was closed.

Again, the social worker cautioned that we should just give her time, that we should not complicate her adjustment by taking her out of the new environment too soon.

All the while, my mother continued to make conversation as though it mattered to her that the wind was or was not blowing, that rain was or was not falling beyond the drawn curtains and her closed eyelids. Her thoughts dwelled more and more with her cousin Rog, who had died of end stage dementia more than a decade before, and though she had not been back to Clinton in over forty years she would tell me, "Everything about the farm is still exactly the same."

So I chatted about the weather while waiting for the go-ahead to take her out even into the courtyard. I brought a plant into her room, and asked for her help watering it. I brought Curtis, the quieter one of my dogs, to sit at her feet for a petting. This routine lasted for a few weeks.

Then my mother fell. And except for the ambulance rides to and from Morana Hospital, she never went outside again.

II .

"What I know now, what I have learned from her, is that there are two forms of death, not one. In one form, everything which holds us in this world, everything we love, may remain precious until the last instant. Everything will stay as it is. Faces will mean what they have always meant to us. In this form of death, life holds all its beauty to the last second.

"Then there is the form of dying in which everything familiar becomes strange, everything known becomes unknown, everything true becomes false, everything loved becomes indifferent, everything pitiful becomes pitiless, everything compassionate becomes as hard as a stone."

-- Michael Ignatieff, *Scar Tissue*

Incident Report

Three weeks to the day after my mother's move to Cascia Hall, I was awakened by the telephone at five A.M. "Your mother fell and hit her head," my father reported. His words were clipped, unnaturally clear. "They took her to Morana Hospital in an ambulance. I'm calling a cab."

My voice contained an edge of irritation that had grown familiar in the eighteen months since Dad had lost his driver's license, months full of dramatic complaints about the inconvenience of taxis. "I'll be there in five minutes; that's why you live five minutes away from us." And then, remembering how frightened he must be by those deceptively ordinary words – *fall, head, hospital* – I remembered to add, "I want to be there for her, too. I love you, Daddy."

That call came nowhere near the start of my mother's lengthy journey through the looking-glass world of Alzheimer's, but it marked the start of her descent into a hell so particular and undeserved that her death five weeks later came almost as a relief.

At some point during the nightmare of Mom's hospitalization, a friend handed me a spoof of a Monopoly card that said, "Get Out of Hell Free." It was still in my jacket pocket the day she died. To "Get Out of Hell Free" was my fondest wish as I helplessly watched my mother plunge into an underworld of delusions and paranoia, as I groped my way through the miasma of round-the-clock caregiving and attempted advocacy for a loved one who was no longer able to speak for herself. Exhaustion, stress, guilt, and an abiding sense of inadequacy made it seem all but impossible to come up for air.

And yet, there are redemptive aspects of nursing a loved one through end-stage dementia: inexplicably, while muddling through crises, making endless mistakes, reaching life and death decisions with inadequate information and a whopping sleep deficit, forgiveness sneaks into your heart and you start remembering the importance of saying "I love you."

When my mother fell, she fell unusually hard. The incident report is full of speculation about what happened, because she was the only witness to her injury. What we know is that she woke sometime after four A.M. in her room at Cascia Hall, that she got up, that she fell. What we surmise is that she intended to go to the bathroom, that she headed towards the wrong door, that she tripped and, because she did not break her fall, her forehead was the first part of her body to make contact with the floor. She yelled for help, but the staff on duty could not enter the room at once because her head was placed like a doorstop against the door. Then the ambulance arrived, paramedics strapped her into a neck-brace and onto a backboard, and by the time my father and I met her at the hospital she was almost unrecognizable. Her forehead had swelled into a massive, overhanging, bloodstained brow and her eyes were firmly closed. Her nose was inflamed, her hair was wild. She was screaming bloody murder.

Beyond immediate anxiety about Mom's condition, that morning loosed a flood of uncomfortable memories, sweeping me back to a time shortly before my grandmother's death. At the age of eighty-five, my mother's mother had hit her head when the car she was riding in crashed. The cousin who was driving and the other passengers were taken to the hospital and released, while Grandma was admitted for observation; because of her age, however, her agitation and confusion caused little alarm. "They just thought she was a babbling old lady," Mom told me later, "when in fact I think she had a brain injury. I think that's what she died from."

Mom flew to New York a few times that summer to meet with her mother's doctors, but for the most part my aunt was in charge of her care. I felt no sense of urgency about visiting Grandma myself. Our telephone conversations followed long-familiar patterns, with my grandmother repeating herself, waxing nostalgic for her childhood, thinking magical thoughts and expecting them to apply to reality. Besides, I was happily preoccupied as my husband and I set off for the honeymoon we had been unable to afford when we were married three years earlier. Flying to Vancouver, we collected a wonderful gift from his parents – a 1973 VW camper van – and headed for the Canadian Rockies.

The summer of 1985 was unusually hot and dry in the high country along the British Columbia - Alberta border. The drought had a paradoxical effect on water levels in mountain streams: the more intensely the sun shone, the more quickly glaciers melted. A couple of days out on the trail, we found ourselves standing on the bank of a raging gray torrent which appeared as a slender thread of creek on our topographic map. We turned back for want of both equipment and expertise to make a safe crossing. The van became our home and haven through sun-dappled days exploring Mt. Robson, Jasper, the Columbia Ice Fields, and crystalline nights cuddling by a campfire. We didn't go out of our way to phone home on rare forays into town.

One night I woke trembling from a dream in which I buried my mother. She lay before me uncovered, eyes closed as if napping. I could smell the raw, turned earth of her grave, feel its dampness in my hand, and hear an odd little ticking sound as the clods I tossed struck her cold skin. Shaken, I insisted on calling her the next day.

The payphone in Jasper had a grubby plastic backing tacked to a light-pole. I called collect and my mother answered, her voice slightly higher than usual. She was fine, she said. Relieved of my dream by the sound of her voice, I launched into a long, starry-eyed celebration of the mountains, of the weight of our packs and the solitude of the trail, of rallying from the disappointment of turning back and reveling in the beauty of now. Silence at the other end of the line. "Is everything OK?" I asked. "Your grandmother died last night," Mom replied.

Stunned, I looked away across the valley. High on the facing slope, parched brush and trees had flared; the air thrummed with the beat of helicopters shuttling water to the blaze. Smoke rose and thinned like the residue of a dream. Had I been stranded on the Moon, I could hardly have felt more distant from my grandmother, who I cared for but had never known well. Yet somehow, in my dream, I had known... not of her death necessarily, but of my mother's loss. It took me so long to find words that Mom assumed

I was speechless with grief; in fact, I was guiltily content not to be there for her once I knew that she was safe.

When my mother fell a quarter of a century later, I had a sense of familial déjà vu: it was my turn to reprise the role she'd played when her mother's head hit the dashboard. Because she was over eighty, Mom's agitation and confusion caused less alarm than they should have when the ambulance rushed her to Morana Hospital. She once looked like Ava Gardner and possessed a piercing wit; now she was just "a babbling old lady." Who had suffered a terrible blow to her already injured brain.

After the Fall

"Norman Harway! You're a bastard! You are the bastardiest bastard in the whole world!"

My mother's voice echoes down hospital corridors as they wheel her (still strapped to a backboard, her neck braced and immobilized two hours after the ambulance dropped her off) from the emergency room to the MRI. "I hate you! I have always hated you! You are letting these people torture me, and you're laughing!"

I stand with my father beside the nurses' station. Grey bearded and stooped, he wears a look of weary resignation. The ER doctor, well over six feet tall and with a ruddy Nordic complexion, towers over him, chuckling. What, I wonder, can anyone find amusing in this scene? The awkwardly inappropriate demeanor of doctors is to become a common feature of our lives in the coming weeks. We are lost and scared, not knowing what to expect. "They're slicing my ears off," shouts my mother. "They're killing me! You're letting them kill me! I hope you and everybody you have ever loved rots in Hell! Fuck you, Norman!"

"Can't you sedate her?" I plead, for the hundredth time. "Not until we have the MRI results," the doctor replies.

Helpless, my father waves his hands at me and says what he has always said, intending to spread oil on the turbulent waters between himself and his outspoken, tactless younger daughter, even though it usually ignites conflict: "Just settle down. Don't get so over-emotional."

Throughout that awful day, I do everything I can to distract my mother, to calm her down. I hold her hands and sing to her, lay a cool cloth across her brow and whisper words of comfort in her ear. I can hardly get her attention. Finally, I mention her favorite cousin with whom she spent childhood summers. "It's good to remember those times," she mumbles, and I respond, "It's good to remember all times."

"What did you say?" she shouts.

I am alarmed. "It's good to remember *all times.*"

"That's what you said? That's really what you said?"

"Yes, Mom. I said 'all times.' What did you think?"

"I thought... I just heard... you said *Alzheims....*"

I said *all times; s*he heard *Alzheimer's.* No matter how disordered and incomplete her thinking, I cannot not redirect her. *Alzheimer's,* the worst word in the world; her greatest fear, her unacknowledged nemesis, the specter my father has willed away and protected her from. Most of a decade after her diagnosis, she lies strapped to a backboard in a hospital emergency room in a city where she will always be a stranger. Trying to tell me what she understands.

That day in the emergency room was perhaps the longest of my life. My father, in a remarkable example of the usefulness of memory loss, has since managed to forget it all, and has now forgotten most everything about my mother's hospitalization.

What I remember of that Wednesday morning is a blur of shouting and cursing, of my mother's accusations ("These people want you to *think* they're doctors! You're as evil as they are!") and recriminations ("If you had a backbone, Norman, you'd help me"), of hospital staff scurrying about ineffectively, and of bruises and bite marks my father and I sustained while trying to keep her from hurting herself as she struggled against restraints. Finally, six hours after she arrived, a nurse came in and injected Valium into my mother's IV line. Moments later, Mom was holding my hands and singing, *"When we kill the old red rooster/ he won't crow like he used-ter..."* Then she fell into a deep and peaceful sleep.

I have attended a number of funerals recently at which my contemporaries eulogize their parents with the observation that Alzheimer's causes you to lose a loved one several times over. Believe me, I know what they mean. I lost my mother again and again over the span of nearly a decade. The day she was admitted to Morana Hospital, however, is the day I began to lose her for the very last time.

"Put Those Dogs Down"

July 2011

It is the summer after my mother's death. Now that both of our children are grown, my husband and I share our home only with two rescued dogs. Boo and Curtis started out as homeless scavengers, and both had the good luck to cross the path of my friend Fran, "St. Fran," a flawless nurturer of lost souls who brought them home to me. Perhaps owing to their harsh beginnings, they are assertive and independent beings who regard "training" as a matter of negotiation between equals. They aren't the dogs most people would choose for urban house pets, but I believe they love us as much as we do them.

My elder dog, Boo, is at least thirteen years old now. One-eyed and gimpy, she wears her graying muzzle and paws with dignity. She was a spirited companion from the day I first met her, a dog who delighted in roaming all day in the north Georgia mountains or chasing deer through Lake Michigan dunes, always checking in every little while to make sure I was still keeping up. Now, though it takes her half an hour to stumble down to the end of the driveway, a couple of houses east or west, across the street on a good day, she still has a spring in her step when I tell her what a good girl she is, making sure my voice is loud enough to reach her old deaf ears.

"You need to put that dog down soon," my father tells me, nearly every time he visits. I ignore the remark, but it hurts. In a lovely piece in *The Bark* magazine, Susan Seligson laments "the blunt, utterly uncensored, and often just plain mean things people say to us about our dogs… When your dog is old and sick, the end is pretty much all you can think about. Your heart is breaking and you're preparing yourself to come to that decision in a way that spares your dog unnecessary suffering while giving yourself time to feel as peaceful as possible about letting him go."

It is a familiar feeling, and not just where my dogs are concerned. In the three years preceding Mom's death, my sister and I had twice over-ridden my father's inclination to take any and all aggressive medical advice, blocking suggested surgical procedures on the grounds that what may be appropriate for a fifty year old in good health would probably have done more harm than good for an eighty-five year old Alzheimer's patient. The first involved removal of a non-cancerous intestinal polyp, and the second was to correct a mild, asymptomatic heart arrhythmia. In both cases, my sister and I believed the trauma and disorientation of hospitalization and recovery would pose a direct threat to our mother's cognitive function, which seemed somewhat stable as long as my father kept her environment and daily routine completely controlled and familiar. Stability trumped longevity in our eyes.

My father's faith in medicine borders on the religious. He did not, could not trust our judgment. On some level, I think he imagined that aggressive medical intervention might keep his wife with him forever. (Ironically, the doctor who sided with us and dissuaded him from proceeding in both instances would later supervise the worst missteps of Mom's final hospitalization.) As in any long marriage, my parents had weathered periods of turbulence, depression and fear, along with great love and accomplishments. Well into their fifth decade together they were, above all, more *married* than almost any couple I have ever known. As they faced the infirmities of old age, I often found myself worrying how one of them could ever live without the other. Alzheimer's only added to their intimate dependence: my mother needed my father to hold her universe together, to protect her from the confusing world outside the apartment door and the fearful disorder inside her own head, to keep her anchored in routine and hold her close in shared memories; my father, for his part, needed the relentless burden of caregiving, of cushioning and controlling every detail of her waking day, to give him a reason to live and distract him from the fact of his own increasing fragility.

Another way I understand my father's unwelcome reminders that dear old Boo is nearing the end of her journey is that he is, of course, struggling to come to terms with my mother's absence. He is a man who prides himself on seeing life through the lenses of reason and intellect, and I am his opposite. I was already an adult before I recognized that his desire to detach from emotion hid a nature equally as raw and sensitive as my own. He would have you believe, however, that even the loss of a spouse after nearly sixty years should be managed with a rational mind.

When Boo's back legs began weakening to the extent that she staggered like a train conductor, I took her to a veterinary neurologist. Assuming that her frailty and lack of coordination in the rear was due either to spinal tumors or to disc deterioration, the doctor outlined complicated tests and possible surgical corrections. I stroked Boo's velvety ears with one hand as she calmly washed my other with her perfect pink tongue, oblivious to the discussion unfolding around her. There was no way I could put her through the trauma of testing, surgery, a long recuperation. She was simply too dear to me. Her life was made narrower by her infirmity, but it is still full of quality and love.

In a strange turn of events, around this same time my younger dog, Curtis, suffered a ruptured disc. One day he was a sprightly, active six year old Basset mix with an endless appetite for hunting chipmunks and mice; the next day he was walking stiffly, and the next his back end completely collapsed. We woke to find him scooting around the house, dragging his limp hind legs behind him.

It was a Sunday so we couldn't see the neurologist. After hesitating to go forward without her assessment of his condition, we were alarmed to see him losing even more ground and arranged for emergency disc surgery that very night. The surgeon called us around three A.M. to report that he had successfully removed "massive amounts of ruptured tissue," and the prognosis for a full recovery was excellent.

My husband joked, "To hell with the federal government: we're raising the debt ceiling in this house." We could legitimately be mocked for spending nearly $4,000 on an operation for our dog in a state where healthcare for the poor is being slashed, but there's a painful irony closer to home: as I nurse Curtis through his long convalescence, Boo gimps gamely around the house, unaware that one of these days, when her back legs give out completely, she will have reached the end of the road. Anyway, a procedure that is appropriate for a six year old dog in good health might do more harm than good for a thirteen year old dog with other physical challenges.

Today, over coffee, I tell my father about how tricky it's been for me to learn how to support Curtis's hind end with a belly sling so he can walk, and to express his bladder while he can't or won't urinate on his own. "I think you're going to have to give up on that dog," he says, "I think it may be time to put him down."

"Nope," I respond to my one surviving parent. And as I look at my dogs stretched out in the gathering dusk, my heart feels full to breaking.

Acute Care

My mother remained under heavy sedation for the first twenty-four hours after admission to Morana. A bed was found for her on an acute care unit, a nexus of well-appointed rooms at the end of an overlong corridor near a two-story lounge that must have been the pride of the brand new hospital.

She had no idea where she was even in her waking moments, and her waking moments were few and far between. Dr. Z, a geriatric psychiatrist who had seen my mother twice over the previous few years, was to supervise her care in consultation with my parents' regular physician, Dr. Y. Initially, she was to be sedated with Valium and optional doses of Haldol and Ativan if she became agitated. (Over the following days, these orders shifted through a menu of tranquilizers and psychotropic drugs: Haldol and Ativan with optional Valium; Seroquel with optional Haldol and Ativan; Risperdal, with optional Haldol and Ativan; Haldol, with optional extra Haldol and Ativan...)

The nurses were, for the most part, kind and hardworking, and they carried a difficult load. I was slow to realize that the option for extra sedation for my mother tended to give the nurse on duty a free pass: when my mother was asleep, it would be a quiet shift in which the nurse could come in, take her vital signs, check her IV and leave the room quickly and safely; when my mother was awake, she might be yelling, throwing things, setting off the bed alarm with her restlessness, requiring (and refusing) assistance with eating and toileting, endlessly pressing the call button just because it was there. These nurses were trained to deal with all manner of physical pain and debility, but they were ill prepared for the challenges of a patient with advanced Alzheimer's; the temptation to simply knock Mom out and leave any potential problems for the next shift was all but irresistible. Dr. Z suggested that my mother might receive more consistent care on the inpatient psychiatric unit where he was based, but my father resisted.

I thought that I kept good notes during the early days of Mom's hospitalization, but when I look at them now I see a bunch of

88

brainless lists: questions for the doctor, things to bring to Mom at the hospital, scheduling my father's visits, arranging for additional overnight care, asking advice from an independent geriatric care consultant, following up with the Cascia Hall social worker, keeping my sister in the loop... though the details blur, for those eight days on the acute care floor my daily schedule was something like this:

Three to five A.M. – Emergency call from hospital reporting that Mom is out of control. Most times I rush down there to calm her and help the nurses administer some drug or another that will knock her out for a few hours. Dr. Z adjusts her meds nearly every day, and the nurses never seem able to administer them on time. Sometimes this is her "midnight dosage;" sometimes her "eight PM dosage" from the night before.

Seven-thirty A.M. – Return to hospital. Debrief with Verna, the private caregiver we've hired to keep an eye on things overnight, and check in with the nurse on duty.

Eight to eleven A.M. – Try to get Mom to toilet, feed her breakfast, brush her teeth, change her underwear... sometimes she lets me help, and sometimes she is immovable. Nurses and aides come and go during this time with meds and food, though they prefer to leave Mom's personal care to me. I usually cannot accomplish much within the span of three hours, and I naively think that whatever I can't get done in this time – for instance a minimal sponge bath for Mom – will be done by staff. After a few days she begins to smell.

Eleven A.M. to four P.M. – During this time, I pick up my father so he can visit Mom for lunch and stay for a few hours. Then I bring him home and return to sit with Mom myself. There are two days when things seem peaceful enough at the hospital and Dad has a caregiver to help with transportation, so I sneak away to my office. I even teach a couple of classes, though it's clear to everyone that I am not on my game. Most days I hunker down for an endless round of phone calling to doctors, social worker, nursing home director, sister, husband, or students I am otherwise ignoring.

Four P.M. – Go home to walk dogs. Sunset comes early in Wisconsin in November, and Mom often dozes in the afternoon. This is my mental health moment, what keeps me going.

Five to six P.M. – Back to hospital, hoping to persuade Mom to eat some of her dinner. When Verna arrives at six, I introduce her to Mom as "my friend Verna who works here at the hospital," the same introduction every night, give her a $20 bill to buy dinner (which costs $6 for a caregiver at Morana), talk with her for a little while, then head home.

Six-thirty P.M.– Feed dogs. Have dinner with husband and/or daughter, whoever is home. Spend the evening on phone calls regarding eldercare options, bringing sister up to date, et cetera.

Nine-thirty P.M. – Call Verna for an update, then collapse into bed.

Three to five A.M. – Emergency call from hospital reporting that Mom is out of control….

Mom's daily schedule, of course, felt nowhere near this orderly. Because the nurses dreaded waking her if she was sleeping, a five P.M. dose of Haldol might not be ingested until eleven. A breakfast tray ordered for seven-thirty A.M. might be served up soggy at ten. If I could boast that I never took a similar shortcut in teaching, this would be the place to do so. Some professions are just profoundly difficult. Most of the acute care nurses were kind, smart, competent women who were woefully over-extended, and my mother was one tough customer. I respect those gals. I trust they did their best.

My mother cannot adapt to the hospital environment. She does not believe my reassurances that the people around us, the people who poke and prod at her, who sometimes refuse to let her rise from the bed, are nurses and doctors. "That's exactly what they *want* you to think," she says.

"OK, Mom: if they're not nurses and doctors, who are they?"

"They're very bad people," she answers. "They do horrible things. The other day, I saw them steal an old lady's pocketbook right out of her shoe."

90

Although moments before she had cursed my father and thrown him out of the room, she seems relatively calm, and this is, at least, a line of conversation. "Why would they do that?" I ask, and she warns, "You have no idea what they will do."

"How did she get her pocketbook into her shoe?"

"Well, she wasn't wearing it at the time. This lady had two pairs."

I don't have the good sense to stop. "But why did she keep it in her shoe?"

"You're my stupid daughter," Mom sighs, explaining with exaggerated clarity: "Because she didn't want those bad people to find it."

I wish I could forget the way Dr. Z rolled his eyes, the brusqueness of his gestures as he pulled a fancy fountain pen out of his breast pocket, tore a sheet from my mother's hospital chart, and wrote:

11/6/10
    For Mr. Harway:
    Plan:
        1) When your wife returns to Umbria Court (sic: Cascia Hall): No visiting x 2 wks
        2) Then visit only at lunch to decrease her evening agitation

I still have that sheet, however, signed in his classic physician's scrawl; he printed his name "legibly" below the signature, and slapped it into my hands, directing me to reinforce his orders if my father couldn't follow them. It was only three days into my mother's hospitalization, and we still hoped that she'd be released very soon. In preparation, Dr. Z kept telling my father to keep his distance. This made so little sense to Dad after six decades of marriage that he simply could not hold the instructions in his brain.

Dr. Z and I stood in the corridor outside my mother's room, and I had just explained how hard this separation would be on my father. Dad can't have been far away as we talked, though I tried to keep him apart from Dr. Z as much as possible. The doctor was not a patient man, and my father's fretfulness got on his nerves: Dad tended to repeat the same question dozens of times, as if hoping for a better answer, and he remembered instructions backwards if they suited him better that way. Thus, he kept insisting that Dr. Z told him *he should never be away* from my mother in the first two weeks after her return to Cascia Hall.

While slightly startled by the length of separation the doctor ordered, I was not surprised that he wanted Dad to stand back and let the nursing home staff help Mom to readjust. His instructions echoed the short-term restrictions on visiting that had ben part of her initial move to Cascia Hall. At that time, I had been comforted by the fact that most residents on her floor appeared contented enough, accepting of their lot. Naively, I looked ahead to a time when each family member would be able to visit my mother as much as we could – my sister every few months; myself three or four times a week; my father nearly all day every day.

Because he relied upon me for transportation, I had control over my father's comings and goings while Mom was hospitalized. He resigned himself to a short mid-day visit as long as I could guarantee that she wouldn't be alone the rest of the time, that either I would be with her or a hired caregiver under my supervision. I feel awful saying this, but orders to limit contact between my parents made my life easier: instead of having to field Dad's obsessive, repetitive questions ("Shouldn't we hire a private nurse? Doesn't she need a private 'round-the-clock nurse? Can't we bring a private nurse into the hospital?"), I could simply tend to Mom's broken record ("Where's Norman?" "He's running a quick errand." "Where's Norman?" "He'll be here soon." "Where's Norman?" "He has a few things to take care of, then he'll be back." "Where's Norman?" Even when Mom was moved to a different floor and Dr. Z banished Dad for three days, my mother lived moment to moment in the belief that he had just stepped out for five minutes). The best reason for keeping my parents apart, however, was nothing like what the doctors intended: because I could open or close the door to Dad at will, he never saw much of Mom screaming at phantoms, throwing food, or clawing at her IV line; he never saw how bad things really got in the hospital.

To preserve his wife's dignity and perhaps his own as well, my father clung to the illusion that somehow, deep inside, she was still herself and still understood what was going on around her. Her odd moments of lucidity fanned the flames of his hope. He hung a cloth over the bathroom mirror on the acute care unit, certain that she would be frightened by her own face, a swollen blood-red mess around the raccoon mask of her two black eyes (she did, in fact, look in the mirror, but didn't recognize the battered face as her own); he balked at Dr. Z's desire to move her to the psychiatric unit, because she had worked as a psychologist and he was sure she would recognize the environment and panic. He comforted her in the language that was comforting to him – lengthy, reasoned explanations of how her recovery was to proceed, with lavish reference to the authority of doctors – at the end of which she would ask, "What is this place?"

When my mother was eventually discharged after sixteen days in the hospital, Dr. Z's old orders that my father should stay away for two weeks were pretty much moot. By that time the distance between Mom and the world in which the rest of us lived had grown significantly greater, as if the slow, heavy cart of oblivion which Alzheimer's set in motion years before had gained sudden, dizzying momentum, careening down a slope that would never level out again.

So my mother's "readjustment" upon returning to Cascia Hall was smoothed by the fact that by then she was forgetting my father along with the rest of us. Of all the regrets that dog me from those sad weeks, none nags as much as the fact that, at Dr. Z's urging, I kept my father away from my mother for two more days, not imagining that she had less than two weeks left to live. Who was I – who was anyone – to step in between them? My father loved my mother in the profound, ungrudging way that marriage vows casually presuppose but all too seldom deliver. She was his reason for living, "'til death do us part."

On one of the two days I get to my office while my mother is in acute care, I return to the hospital in late afternoon to find her shrieking curses, striking her chest with her fists. I catch her hands in mine. "I'm a horrible, horrible person," she moans.

Surely, this is a new delusion, but my heart feels torn in two: this guilt is real to her, it's eating her up. To distract her, I start talking about my dogs. I have no idea whether or not she remembers them, but she loves dogs in general and always has a few genial stock phrases to fall back on. "Let me tell you what my dog Curtis did this morning," I often say, anticipating her automatic response: "That dog is such a stinker!"

Miraculously, the distraction works. I help her up out of her chair to go to the toilet. She forgets to make her usual paranoid comments about the chair alarm as I disconnect it. ("They don't want you to get up. They control your every movement here." "They want you to be safe, Mom," is my usual answer, though I see the logic of her fears.) We labor across the room. Because Mom keeps her eyes closed nearly all the time these days, it is no easy matter to guide her; she tends to veer to the right in a circle, and yells at any piece of furniture with which she collides. At last we maneuver into the bathroom, and I help her settle on the toilet seat.

She urinates, I wipe her. As I help her to her feet again, she cycles back into that earlier paranoid thought. "I'm such a bad person that I deserve to die," she remarks almost matter-of-factly.

I come back with everything a daughter could say under the circumstances: *You are a wonderful person, Mom, a wonderful mother. You have a beautiful heart. You should have no regrets. You have touched so many people's lives; you have made such a difference....*

"You shut up," she snaps, shoving me away. "You have no idea of the things I've done."

A strange, unwelcome thought creeps into my mind: *She's right. I have no idea of the things she's done.* Even when my mother was whole we would never have confided in one another about matters that caused us to inwardly cringe: childhood guilts or

94

common regrets, obscure nooks of the mind where we cached our darkest thoughts, hard little abscesses of shame on the heart. For one perverse moment I wonder what she might confess to if pressed, but what I say is, "It's OK now, Mom. I'm right here beside you. I love you."

She strikes me hard in the chest, yelling, "What the hell do you know? I know what I've done. It's horrible. I'm horrible. I deserve to die. No, even death is too good for me!"

My tears keep me from arguing, although she is well beyond noticing. We stumble back to the bed. As I help lift her legs up onto the mattress, she seems to breathe a little easier. "Let me tell you what Curtis did this morning," I murmur, stroking her hair, and she automatically responds, "That dog is such a stinker!"

My mother still has moments of high spirits, particularly when she sings. As she settles down for a nap, I leave her singing to the white walls, to the drawn blinds, to the covers pulled up to her chin, to the nurses shuffling in the hall, to all the beeping monitors, *"From the Halls of Montezuma / to the shores of Tripoli...."*

I come straight back to the hospital after a few hours at my office. It is dark outside, sleet falling. The halls buzz with fluorescence, and my mother sits weeping silently in a chair.

"What's the matter, Mom?"

"I'm so tired," she sobs, "I'm tired all the way down to the second level of my mind."

The Mind of Another Person

As part of their graduate education, my parents interned at the Veterans Administration Hospital in Canandaigua, NY. In the years after World War II, VA hospitals were overwhelmed with traumatized vets, so they were logical sites for training those entering the young field of Clinical Psychology.

Decades later, as a college student, I spent a summer working part-time at the Pittsburgh Child Guidance Center, where my mother was Director of Consultation and Education. Until that summer, I had experienced her career from a distance, trying my adolescent best to tune out the remarkable stories of human drama and suffering that she and my father exchanged over dinner each evening; now that I had a front row seat, I was filled with grudging pride at the evident respect with which she was regarded by colleagues, and I remember beginning to ask more questions. Over lunch one day, she told me a story about how she learned to administer psychological tests during her internship. The tests were basic inventories on which the respondent checked yes or no to questions like: "Do you often feel scared? Do you have trouble falling asleep? Do you think you hear voices?" My mother was assigned to a locked ward on which many of the men were profoundly disturbed, but when she tested them, the craziest guy on the unit came up with a perfectly sane score. "I knew something had to be wrong," she said, "but I didn't have the experience to recognize what it was."

"What was wrong?" I asked, and she explained: the questions presupposed the sanity of the asker and the insanity of the answerer. But this particular patient was only willing to answer questions on his own terms. Thus, after checking *yes* or *no*, he qualified each answer with notes in the margins that had been overlooked in the scoring –

"Do you often feel scared?" *No. I always feel scared.*

"Do you have trouble falling asleep?" *No. I don't sleep at all.*

"Do you think you hear voices?" *No. I know I hear voices.*

This conversation rose from my memory many times throughout my mother's struggle with Alzheimer's. When she told me the story, she probably meant to remind me that the answers we receive depend upon the questions we ask, but the moral I take from it now is sadder and more nuanced. We can reach out to one another with the kindest intentions, with love and support, but we cannot count on making a connection. We can never truly know what is going on in the mind of another person.

After my sophomore year, I transferred from a massive Big Ten campus to a small liberal arts college in New England. The daughter of some family friends started as a freshman there that same fall, and I took a big-sisterly interest in her, checking in frequently and inviting her over for dinner now and then. We had little in common, but Amber was a nice kid and I kind of enjoyed feeling responsible for her.

Her first few weeks of college shone: she loved dorm life, loved her classes, liked her roommate Cecily, and tolerated my attempts to mother her. But as September gave way to October, strange things started happening. Amber came home one day to find that her dorm room had been ransacked, and her roommate's things were strewn all over the floor. Then someone started placing threatening calls to Cecily. Then the bathroom mirror was smeared with lipstick lettering: "Fuck Cissy." When the window screen (first floor, facing a large expanse of woods) was slashed in the night, I told Amber that she needed to stay at my apartment until campus security got to the bottom of this. She refused for fear that her roommate would be unsafe without her.

I never told my parents about this because I felt sure, with the wisdom of my nineteen years, that they would worry too much and blow the whole thing out of proportion. Amber told her parents some things, but edited out the worst. There was a major investigation on campus, which, after a short time, came to focus on the roommate herself: why were the threatening phone calls received only when she was home alone? Why was the window screen slashed from the inside out?

97

In short order, the mystery unraveled: Cecily had developed psychosis. The stalker was a delusion, which she believed in so fervently that she was, in effect, stalking herself. After the roommate was dismissed from the college, Amber moved to another dorm and I was left wondering – I still am wondering – what constitutes a *delusion*? For the person who is *always scared*, who sees dark forms moving among the trees because she *doesn't sleep at all*, who *knows that she hears the voices* of whomever is stalking her, is this not a reality?

I'm writing about mental illness here, which is not the same thing as dementia. Manifestations such as delusions or paranoia can be symptomatic of either, but there is one key difference: much mental illness, with proper care, therapy and medication, can potentially be treated so that a person can lead a full life; Alzheimer's dementia may be controlled briefly, but there is no treatment to speak of. The disease will run its course in its own time. Although experts have identified stages of Alzheimer's, the duration of those stages varies widely from patient to patient, and not all patients will experience all identifiable stages. Is there ever a "textbook case" of any disease? The only guarantee with Alzheimer's is the outcome: this is not a disease that anyone survives.

Recently, I've been following a tragic story in the news: in Erin, Wisconsin, an eighty-five year old man was charged with attempted homicide, but was at first deemed incompetent to stand trial. The intended victim was his wife of sixty-five years. Because of his failing health, the couple had decided to move into an assisted living facility; anticipating his own death, he told a relative that he could not imagine how his beloved could live without him. On the night of June 23, 2011, he repeatedly struck her on the head with a hammer then swallowed a massive cocktail of pills to finish the job for himself. For better or for worse, nobody died that night: the wife came to and called 9-1-1, and paramedics were able to resuscitate the husband.

By all accounts, Charles McNeer is a man with an impeccable, all-American record: he grew up in the West Virginia coalfields, served in WWII, graduated from Northwestern University, and rose through corporate ranks to eventually head Wisconsin's largest utility. He was known as a generous philanthropist, a pillar of his community. When I first read this story, I immediately jumped to the conclusion that he was suffering from Alzheimer's, because his age, his paranoia, his disjointed thinking, and his violent outburst made sense to me in light of what I have witnessed. I assumed that the poor guy's dementia had reached a delusional stage, convincing him that the world was out to get him. That he was trying to take his wife with him seemed a peculiarly touching detail.

My assumptions did not stop there: based upon my mother's experience, I was willing to bet that the psychiatric hospital where he was held in an effort to make him "competent" to stand trial was no place for a person with his problems, any more than the behavioral health unit to which my mother was eventually transferred proved to be a therapeutic environment for her. The psychiatric nurses who cared for my mother seemed no better prepared to work with Alzheimer's patients than the acute care nurses (and the one nurse I encountered who claimed expertise in this area was the most woefully unprepared of all). Psychotropic drugs can control behavior by sedating an Alzheimer's patient into numb oblivion, but there will never be any improvement in cognitive function.

McNeer's story, as it turns out, is not quite what I presumed. Initially judged incompetent to stand trial, he was remanded to a state psychiatric facility where, after treatment with anti-psychotic drugs, the court modified its determination. As I write this, the newspapers report that he is "responding to treatment" for depression and psychosis, and a decision is forthcoming about whether he will stand trial for the attempted murder of his wife. What anyone gains from this scenario is beyond me.

I can't quite back down from my initial assumptions about this case, despite the fact that all expert testimony challenges what I think I know from experience. If someone attempts to murder his wife and then take his own life, he's crazy, right? No argument there. But what if that someone is an octogenarian who has lived a sane and stable life? As longevity increases and the population ages, both dementia and deep depression come with the territory. My mind worries these questions like a bulldog worries a bone: how do we plan to care for our elders? Where will we keep them? How will we understand them?

Soon enough, needless to say, *we will be them.*

Caregiving 101

My great aunt in Ireland is ninety-five years old and lives in a nursing home. After the death of her husband, her increasingly complex health problems made it impossible to live independently. Her daughter, a painstaking and determined caregiver, still faults her brother for placing their mother in the hands of "strangers." It's not that my aunt is unhappy – she is comfortable, well-fed, living in a cheerful environment; she enjoys flirting and holding hands with her new gentleman friend, a handsome man ten years her junior who suffered a cataclysmic stroke. No, what troubles my cousin is that she believes that elders should be cared for by the family. This is the way families have managed since the beginning of time, she says; we must care for our own. The details mean a lot to my cousin: underwear tends to dim from a brilliant white to something less than brilliant after a few weeks of institutional laundering; an aide might forget to offer her mother's customary glass of port before bed. What really blows my mind about these complaints is that in addition to excellent care from the staff, my aunt usually receives *two visits per day* from relatives. How can this be construed as neglect?

Around the time we moved my mother to Cascia Hall, I confessed to the geriatric care consultant my guilt at being unable, or unwilling, to take Mom into my home and care for her on my own. She, in turn, posed a resonant question to me: did I want to be my mother's primary caregiver, or did I want to know that my mother was well cared for and spend time with her simply as a daughter? There is a significant distinction here: to be a caregiver means to be preoccupied with endless chores and to enforce many things that may seem unpleasant in the moment (bathing, medicines, structured meals, appointments, and so on), while to be simply a daughter or son means to be a comforting presence who connects your parent to shared experiences and memories, to many layers of the past that s/he may be losing. Caregivers give care; children, no matter how old, have the potential to give joy.

Of course I came down on the side of being my mother's daughter. Any number of people could wash her bottom, I reasoned, but only a daughter could coax her into remembrance of intimate moments and private jokes that were known to no one beyond our immediate family. Besides, this construct gave me a very modern and easy way out: though I would visit my mother for a finite period every day, my life would still be my life, my time would still be my time, my home would still be my home. Not a bad deal.

Caregiving for an elder is often likened to parenting one's parents. There are so many ways, however, in which this analogy fails. Parenting a child is a joyful, growing act, while caring for an elderly parent means staring into the face of mortality. Besides, young children want to be parented, while most elders chafe at the loss of independence, the shift in the family balance. Parenting a child can be so redemptive and hopeful that you may as well be nurturing yourself; parenting a parent reminds you, at every turn, of what you cannot do, what you cannot save, as life winds down inexorably towards death.

When I think of Verna, the caregiver who stayed with my mother every evening for the last five weeks of her life, the word that comes immediately to mind is *smooth*. Not smooth like a roué or pool-shark or politician – smooth like egg custard, like a friend massaging your neck, like Ella Fitzgerald's voice. Verna was comfort incarnate.

Though my parents had signed on with an eldercare agency eighteen months earlier, I had been unimpressed by the individuals sent to help them with shopping and chores. The one man, my father's favorite, was the caricature of a flaming gay out-of-work actor, an exuberantly charming guy who talked too fast and had no sense of boundaries; the women ranged from a stolid Polish granny who treated Mom like a toddler, to a vibrant church-lady who kept her quiet by singing hymns and preaching whenever Dad was out of earshot. None of these people was a "fit" for my parents, culturally or educationally, at a time of life when my parents could not adapt themselves to "fit" others around them. But how fussy could we be? The agency sent us people of good will, people who would not rob or mistreat elderly clients. It was hard to justify rejecting someone for being a little loud, for not always listening, for not meshing well with my parents because of a lack of education – particularly when, despite the agency's charge of $22 per hour, a caregiver earned something like $8.50.

Then came Verna. Unlike the other caregivers, I didn't even try to pick Verna, didn't interview her, and didn't observe her in action before making a commitment. My mother was stuck in the hospital and out of control; we needed someone to sit with her overnight, so we took whomever the agency sent, sight unseen. When Verna arrived that first evening, I glimpsed her from a distance, a petite African-American woman walking down the endless corridor in a relaxed, unhurried way, her hair falling around her shoulders in shiny ringlets, her quilted orange vest half-zipped. She looked like a teenager lost in daydreams. As she drew closer and into focus, however, it became clear that she was a woman of at least my age. The ringlets were a wig. The unhurried, day-dreamy manner was the essence of Verna.

Though Verna grew up in Alabama the only resonance of the deep South in her voice was a matter of pacing. She talked slowly, seeming to think through the words as she said them, and responded to others with a steady, empathetic stream of *um-hums*. In early adulthood, she had somehow landed in Brooklyn, which had a pronounced impact on her accent and inflection, and then she and her husband followed factory jobs to Milwaukee. They raised four children, divorcing along the way, although they still lived together because she feared he could not make it on his own. One of her daughters, who had two children of her own, adopted two more, the younger of whom has Down's syndrome. Having recently been laid off from her job in the mailroom of a prominent Milwaukee bank, Verna found great joy in nurturing her new grandchild with special needs. This is where she got the idea that she might have a future in caregiving.

Eldercare, like caring for children, is a minimum wage job in our society. But Verna had the strength to define her availability according to her values. Though she never told me much about her church, her commitment was clear: she preferred to work late shifts or care for clients overnight so that she could be free to pursue good works of her own choosing during the day.

Moments after we met, I introduced Verna to Mom as "my friend who works here at the hospital and wants to visit with you," an introduction I repeated every night. Mom seemed to like her. I liked her. I had no idea how much I would come to love her in the weeks ahead.

If my mother had been intact, she would have recognized the cultural distance between Verna and herself. Both were smart and strong women, but my mother pursued formal education with a red-hot passion, while Verna had limited schooling and set her sights on the practical goal of simply making sure she could feed her kids. My mother had challenged her upbringing by raising us to respect people of different races and backgrounds; Verna had grown up in the Jim Crow south, understanding the importance of respecting one's self no matter what.

Verna seemed to get my mother like a good joke. Though born too late to have witnessed the Jazz Age or the Swing Era, she knew every song that mattered to Mom. Moreover, she understood the essence of family. When she could coax my mother to reminisce about her grandparents, her aunts and uncles, her cousins, her parents, Verna would lapse into contented silence, punctuated by those quiet *um-hum*s.

Every evening when Verna arrived at the hospital, I'd breathe a sigh of relief: I could go home and get some sleep, knowing that someone I trusted was watching over my mother. It was not lost on me that the "emergency" calls in the night were always from the hospital nurses: Verna was able to see that my mother was more frightened than frightening, and she focused on calming Mom down herself instead of calling in the cavalry. When my mother flared up and threw her out of the room, Verna would respond, "OK. I'm going now. But I'll be back in just a few minutes because I love you." However much Mom screamed and shouted, Verna always returned moments later and greeted her as if she was a long lost sister. After a few well-considered questions, and maybe a song from the forties, the two of them would be sitting side by side on the bed, as Verna gently eased my mother down to rest again.

What did Verna have that so many other caregivers do not? I keep coming back to her sense of self-worth. Whatever her life had lacked in privilege and education, she comfortably approached everyone – my mother, the nurses, myself – as her equal. In this, she reminded me of the finest babysitter we hired when our kids were young, a woman who has come to be one of my closest friends – after meeting her for the first time my husband joked that though the ideal applicant to care for our children need not speak English, she must be smart, soulful, and blessed with a strong sense of purpose. I answered that, when hiring a caregiver, why not hire someone who is everything you hope for your child to be?

Caregiving for an elder with dementia is a task that often seems divorced from hope. The "progress" of Alzheimer's is a process of diminishment, and the manifestation of the disease is anything but lovable. Verna refused to see my mother as diminished. When she told Mom she'd come right back "because I love you," she truly meant it. She was never preachy about faith, race, money, class, or her own complicated life story. Her demeanor embodied an ethic based on compassion, a deep sense of justice and forgiveness. I'm sure, in Verna's own eyes, she simply tries to be a good Christian.

The cultural disconnect between caregivers and patients was a constant feature of my mother's nursing home care. At Cascia Hall, all of the patients were affluent, well educated, and white. The senior administrators were also white and educated; the nursing staff was racially mixed to a limited degree; the aides who had the most consistent contact with patients were, with very few exceptions, women of color and modest education. I'm sure you would see a similar social constellation at the majority of upscale nursing facilities in the United States. Had my mother still been the woman she was when I was growing up, she would have consciously avoided stereotyping based upon race or background. She would have appreciated each person for him or herself. But my mother had slipped so far back through time she was again a child who sang rhymes about "the Chinaman" as she jump-roped double Dutch in the streets of Queens. The aides at Cascia Hall treated her with a respect and consideration she was no longer able to reciprocate.

By contrast, in the nursing home where my Irish aunt resides, there is no cultural divide between staff and residents: the homogeneity of the country is highlighted in a small rural town. While the depredations of Alzheimer's look much the same the world over, my husband and I were struck by the harmony between caregivers and patients in St. Anthony's Manor. There was always a tea trolley available, always a few biscuits on hand, and no one minded that one old gent occupied hours pouring out cup after cup for himself, then losing each in plain sight. Late in the evening, aides served a mug of beer or a glass of sherry to residents who customarily enjoyed a nightcap before bed – my aunt counts on her glass of port. Although my cousin may feel that her mother is in the care of "strangers," from my perspective she is in the care of children just like hers in the village where she has spent all but a few of her ninety-five years.

While visiting Ireland in the spring of 2011, what stood out for me in my aunt's nursing home was the piano. Cascia Hall had a piano, and a volunteer came in once a week to play old favorites during the lunch hour; the St. Anthony's piano got daily exercise. Someone from the community led a sing-along every few days, and residents sometimes wheeled themselves up to the keyboard to play a tune or two. Given a little encouragement to overcome her false modesty, my aunt could hammer out a mean "Onward Christian Soldiers." Music was an unscheduled, impromptu gift. In the tradition of Irish *craic,* both residents and staff seemed ready for a party on a moment's notice.

The first time my Irish aunt met my husband, she took me aside and said, "Judy, you've married a lovely man," a pronouncement made sweeter by her accent: "*a loovely mahn.*" The fact that he is a musician added to her approval. Over many visits, he has played through the reams of crumbling sheet music she saved from her youth, music her arthritic fingers were no longer capable of negotiating. Every time we arrive, her warm greeting is followed by, "Play the piano for me, Dan!"

So, when we came to see her at St. Anthony's Manor, he played the piano. In his words:

> *I sat down at the electronic piano in the main sitting room and, this being Ireland, I tried to recall a lovely arrangement of "Danny Boy" by Bill Evans I'd transcribed years ago. I noodled around a bit, transposing to a new key with each verse as in Evans' performance. The final chord's digital reverb had hardly died when she said, a little impatiently, "Play more. Don't stop."*

The way I remember the scene is that the moment my husband struck the first note, the whole place lit up: nurses and aides scurried to bring residents out of their rooms, elders gathered near the piano shouted requests. When she heard "Danny Boy," a woman seated on the other side of my aunt proudly proclaimed, "There are ten Dan's in my family, so this is my favorite song."

> *I began "Cockles and Mussels," and heard some voices singing along. One of the participants was a gentle man I'd talked to earlier, a stroke victim with severe speech impairment* (my aunt's new beau*). Though compromised in his diction, his pitch and projection were quite impressive so I began singing, too, and between us we inspired more voices to join in. The staff began to bring more folks from their rooms to what was now becoming an event; as the crowd gathered, I began searching a few sheet music books and asking for suggestions. Then I'd launch bravely into songs like "The Rose of Tralee," discovering quickly that I*

didn't know the bridge, nonetheless getting dragged through all three verses. "It's a Long Way to Tipperary" was a rouser, though I discovered that around here it's customary to make quite an elegant segue to "Pack Up Your Troubles In Your Old Kit Bag."

My husband notes that when he ran out of ideas he "found that repeating songs was quite accepted by the memory-challenged audience." He played "Danny Boy" again and again, and each time the woman beside my aunt leaned across and told me, "There are ten Dan's in my family, so this is my favorite song."

"Ten Dan's!" I exclaimed finally. "This must be a very special song for you."

"Aye, it is," the woman responded, ticking off on her fingers the relationships between each of the Dan's and herself. After naming the tenth Dan, she laid her hand affectionately upon my aunt's arm and told me, "And this here is my husband Vincent."

"Get off of me," my aunt grumbled, pushing away her neighbor's hand. "I didn't marry a 'Dan'," the other woman continued dreamily, patting my aunt's forearm, "I fell for my Vincent here."

My aunt turned to me in exasperation. "Don't mind this one, Judy: she's a loon."

The face of Alzheimer's dementia is the same the world over. In Cascia Hall, my mother fought back phantoms, while her neighbors cried out to go home, lamenting than no one cared for them despite the twenty-four hour attentions of aides and nursing staff; in St. Anthony's Manor, many of my aunt's contemporaries continually set off chair alarms with their efforts to walk out and check the crops, wailing at long-dead family members to bring the ponies in because it looks like rain. In both environments, music was tonic, and I wish my mother had enjoyed more live music in her last days. Recalling our visits to St. Anthony's, my husband writes,

108

*I experimented successfully with non-Irish favorites like
"Loch Lomond" and "Over the Rainbow." The noise level
was growing not just with the number of voices, but from
the loud electronic alarms attached to the chairs of the
residents with limited mobility who wanted to get up and
dance... we ended the evening gracefully with a heartfelt
"Auld Lang Syne."*

When I think of those sing-alongs at St. Anthony's Manor, I
linger on my aunt's face, smiling through her tears as my husband
stumbled through "Come Back to Erin" for the dozenth time. I
cherish the sight of a few young aides inviting patients to waltz
when he played "I Could Have Danced All Night," and as we said
goodbye, the whoops and hollers as the director of nursing
launched into a spirited Highland Fling. My mother would have
loved it.

Every night that my mother spent on the acute care unit, Verna
arrived at six P.M. and left at eight in the morning. A fourteen hour
shift. She always brought something to read, wore comfortable
clothes, and asked the nurses for an extra blanket. If she slept at all,
it would have been on the fold out chair in the corner of Mom's
room. If I accidentally left my cell phone turned off overnight,
Verna did not hesitate to scold me roundly.

When Mom later moved to the behavioral health unit, Dr. Z
grudgingly allowed Verna to stay with her through the first night.
Then, over the doctor's objections, my sister and I continued to
hire Verna from six to nine P.M. because Mom needed a familiar
and loving voice, and we needed an extra set of eyes and ears
during the most volatile hours of the evening. My mother never
remembered Verna's name, but she seemed comfortable in her
presence, and Verna knew Mom's foibles well enough that they
got along like gangbusters.

When my mother finally returned to the nursing home, Verna
returned with her. Whether or not Mom was aware of this
continuity is anyone's guess: by then she was at a loss to recognize

her own family, let alone a good-hearted "stranger." Despite my upbringing and education, I felt very insecure about my ability to support my mother through her decline; Verna had such an easy manner that my mother naturally felt safe with her.

From the first night of my mother's hospitalization until the last night of her life, for five weeks without a single night off, Verna was there.

Caregiving for someone you love with Alzheimer's is a dicey proposition. When the diagnosis comes, the only guarantee you have is that you can't protect that sweet someone from gradually forgetting everything that has ever mattered to him or her before dying in isolation. That's an ugly sentence, but true. Moreover, when you step up to the plate as the caregiver, you embrace the guarantee that you will feel helpless, that you will fail at what you most desperately want to do, because there is no graceful way to accompany a loved one on this painful, unwarranted journey into oblivion.

What would I do to improve the lot of Alzheimer's patients? The question echoed in my thoughts as I watched my mother dying and felt frighteningly aware of my own lack of coping strategies. Like countless other daughters and sons, I did my best: I fought back hard against my mother's forgetting, revisiting family albums, retelling her life to her as I had heard it. And, like countless other daughters and sons, I balanced my passionate desire to anchor my mother in the here and now with an equally compelling desire to stay anchored in my own life, to not lose sight of my own needs, my family's needs, the essential grounding rhythms of daily life.

If I could change the face of Alzheimer's care, I think this would be my ideal: every Alzheimer's patient would be treated with infinite patience and forbearance. If the patient reverses day and night, day and night remain reversed until and unless the patient returns to being diurnal. If the patient refuses bathing, assistants will gently cajole her into memories and games involving water so that a basic measure of hygiene is maintained. If the patient forgets her own children, there will be no stigma attached to the substitution of a doll or a cat as the object of affection that reconnects her to the deep vein of nurturance that defines one as a parent. If the patient neglects to eat or cannot conform to a regular schedule of meals, the caregivers will stuff their pockets full of tempting snacks and treats, laying aside concerns for balanced nutrition in the interests of encouraging adequate calorie consumption to stay alive. In short, all care will be flexible, highly individualized, and finely tuned to whimsy so that the environment will conform to the moment in which the patient exists. And the next moment. And the next.

Shortly after my mother's death, the *New York Times* ran an article titled "Giving Alzheimer's Patients Their Way, Even Chocolate." Using an Arizona nursing home called Beatitudes as its focus, the article profiled a "revolutionary" approach to Alzheimer's care in which "dementia patients... are allowed practically anything that brings comfort, even an alcoholic 'nip at night.'" Among the "good non pharmacological techniques" discussed are no-brainers like flexibility about food and scheduling, "helping caregivers to be more accepting," and "engaging patients in activities that salvage fragments of their skills." Individualized engagement is favored over group activities "in which few residents could actually participate." The Beatitudes model relies on some perceptual trickery – for instance placing "a rectangle of black carpet in front of the dementia unit's... elevators because residents appear to interpret it as a cliff or hole, no longer darting into elevators and wandering away" – but the overall focus is on avoiding heavy use of anti-psychotic drugs, keeping residents out of diapers and restraints, and honoring each individual's identity. With this approach, "there is virtually no sundowning" says Jan Dougherty, director of family and community services at Banner Alzheimer's Institute in Phoenix.

When all is said and done, Cascia Hall was and is a very good nursing home. Though it was not staffed to the extent that would be necessary for the Beatitudes model of care to work successfully, the aides and nurses were flexible to the best of their ability. If my mother had never fallen, I'm pretty sure she would have continued

111

her pattern of growing agitated late in the day, and the staff might have needed some measure of pharmacological support to control her behavior, regardless of how flexible and caring they were... Once she fell and was admitted to the hospital, however, the sole focus of treatment shifted to pharmacological management of behavior.

As I read that article in the *Times* about innovations in Alzheimer's care, I was carried back to St. Anthony's Manor, to the environment in which my aunt is tended by the children of her village. Her daughter may feel guilty about sharing the burden of eldercare with paid assistants, but I was deeply heartened by what I saw. My aunt is a retired farmer's wife; her son is a farmer, her daughter a housewife married to an electrician: despite their intelligence and political awareness, they would readily tell you that they are simple people, working people. They disdain any sense of exceptionalism.

My parents also were born to modest circumstances. Through their education, hard work, and assimilationist energy, they earned substantial privilege in American society. They provided their children with elite educational opportunities, helped us financially as we started families of our own, and ensured that we would be able to care for them in their dotage without sacrificing our own careers and lives. The care that my mother received at Cascia Hall may not have been perfect, but it was never lacking. And my sister and I were in a position to provide extra support.

Some years before my aunt entered nursing home care, I found myself in an extended discussion with two of her adult granddaughters about maternity leave. I casually described the options I had faced as a young American mother – six weeks of paid leave, which could extend longer if my child was born in summer when I was not expected to be in the classroom anyway – and was startled by the looks on my cousins' faces. In Ireland at that time, the guarantee of maternity leave was twenty-six weeks paid, with an additional sixteen weeks as needed. Throughout the developed world, maternity benefits exceed what is offered to parents in the United States: up to three years in the Czech Republic, Slovakia, and Austria, sixteen to eighteen months in Sweden and Estonia, fifty-two weeks throughout most of the United Kingdom. My cousins exchanged expressions of distress and pity, then turned back to commiserate with me.

Though I would not change the circumstances of my birth, I have learned to take nothing for granted. My sister and I were born in a ridiculously wealthy country to loving parents with the means and desire to support our aspirations unconditionally. Though my Irish cousins were born into less affluent circumstances, it was evident that they relied upon the shared social value of extending good care to everyone, regardless of means, as a hallmark of national identity. In this, they were not radical or presumptuous; they were simply normal citizens of their time and place.

The Irish system would work well for Verna, my mother's guardian angel. Unfortunately, though, she lives in a country where access to health insurance is tied to employment, and she works in an industry that provides little or no healthcare benefits to employees. Her income places her below the poverty line. As I write this, Badger care, the Wisconsin state program that provides coverage to the poor and uninsured, is being eviscerated by Governor Scott Walker's administration. What care will be available for Verna, I wonder, when her health and her memory fail; what support will society offer to her and her family at the end of life?

More Scenes from Acute Care

The figures she sees lurking in the shadows, in the corners, terrify her. "Go away!" my mother shouts, "I told you to get out!"

But they won't go away. "I'm here," I tell her, "and I'll keep you safe."

"Oh no! That means they'll get you, too," she cries. "These are very dangerous people. They'll stop at nothing."

For the most part, I have been successful at chasing ghosts out of her hospital room, but these specters are not inclined to leave peacefully. "What do you think we should do?" I ask.

"We have to call the police," she says. Then, grabbing an invisible telephone off the bedside table, she stage whispers into the 'receiver:' "Operator, put me through to the police station closest to where we are now." She waits for the call to connect, says thank you, then reports, "You need to send somebody here right now. It's an emergency." Turning to me, she asks, "Where are we?"

"Morana Hospital."

Then she's back on the phone: "We're at Morana Hospital," she says, "We were here earlier but I left something, and when I came back to get it I found this horrible, horrible person *pretending to be me.*"

What is this that I am witness to? The woman I am sitting with in this room at Morana Hospital bears little resemblance to the mother I have known all my life. It's as if she's straining after metaphor to explain the depth of betrayal by her own mind. "You have to hurry," she urges, "we're in danger. This is a horrible person I'm talking about."

Then she pauses, listening hard as whatever voice she hears instructs her. "Thank you very much," she nods, "we'll do exactly as you say." She 'hangs up' and turns to me. "They're sending someone right over."

Caught between laughter and tears, I stammer, "It's OK now, Mom, we're safe."

114

"Did they go away?" she asks, and I sigh. "Yes, they're gone. I ordered them to get out."

My mother grabs my hand, eyes shining like a searchlight: " I knew you could do it! That's my big brave girl!"

At six P.M. it is long since dark. The moon is rising. This worries me because I've heard many times that full moons and long nights don't agree with Alzheimer's patients, and here is my mother, languishing in the hospital beneath a full moon as the winter solstice approaches. I go home after work to let the dogs out, say hello to my husband, and rush back to the hospital. My mother is sitting in the blue recliner, singing to herself. "What are you singing, Mom?" I ask, and her answer surprises me: "It's a dirty song."

This is too sweet to resist. "How does it go?" She throws back her head and sings:

I'd like to be a fascinating lady
With a life that is fast and a past that is shady
I'd live in a house with a little red light
I'd sleep all day and I'd work all night
And once a month I'd take a brief vacation
To drive all my customers wild

(this last line is accompanied by a florid gesture and a crazy trill of the voice)

I'd like to be a fascinating lady
Instead of a legitimate child....

A nurse comes in. Dinner is delivered. Verna arrives, and I am preparing to leave. Suddenly, Mom is singing the song again under her breath.

"What are you singing?" I ask.

She looks sheepish. "It's a dirty song."

"How does it go?"

115

"Who do you think I am?" she snaps, "I wouldn't sing a song like that to *you.*"

Around noon one day there is a vigorous knock at the door of Mom's room. In the corridor, I find a short, grey-haired woman in a mousey cardigan, a white blouse, and a woolen skirt that is almost long enough to conceal her running shoes. "I'm Sister Mary Columba," she tells me, slipping the rosary she carries into her pocket so she can check her clipboard. "I'm a volunteer, and I'm here to visit Vivian Harway."

"Who's there?" my mother hollers from her bed, having woken enough to notice me stepping out. "I'll be right back, Mom," I call, but she is irate. "Someone's there and I know it," she shouts, "now: *Who is there?*"

Before I can stop her, the little nun pushes past me and enters my mother's room. "Are you Vivian?" she asks. Sounding like the moll from an old gangster movie, my mother snarls, "Who wants to know?"

My mother had a traditional Catholic girlhood, but left the church before she married. She embraced the Jewish customs her husband had grown up with, raising her own daughters in a quirky hybrid household: if asked, we introduced ourselves as Jews, though a perfectly prepared Passover Seder might be followed, a few days later, by a ham on Easter Sunday. Now, with Mom's usual level of confusion heightened by the disorienting hospital environment, I have no idea how she might react to a do-gooder intent on bringing Christ on the cross to her bedside.

"Mom," I cry, rushing into the room, "This lady's a nun. Do you want a visit from a nun?" The good sister smiles at her hopefully.

"A *nun?*" Mom shoots back, as though shocked by a dirty word. "I don't want any nuns in here! Make her go away. I don't like nuns." I can't help smiling: while it's true that my mother had some bad memories of punishments meted out in her parochial grade school, she also expressed respect for the idealism of women who used their religious vocation to teach and to tend the sick and

116

poor in times when both educational opportunities and career options for women were scarce.

I shrug and follow Mary Columba back into the corridor. She interrupts my apology with a kindly pat on my arm. "I don't take it personally: your mother is in pain. Do you mind if I pray for her and for you?"

Through a sudden wash of tears I tell her, "We need all the help we can get."

Another morning I arrive to find a hospital aide, a heavyset woman with a very loud voice, trying to coax my mother to the bathroom. "Take your paws off me, you pig," Mom hollers. I mumble apologies as the woman persists, but Mom is having none of it. "Get this one out of here! She's a fat pig."

Drawn by the yelling, a young nurse comes in. She leans close to Mom's ear, speaks very softly. Mom whimpers and huffs a little, but calms down. "Come on," says the pretty, young nurse, helping my mother to rise, "it's been a long time since you went to the toilet. Now is a good time to pee."

My mother is affronted. "Were you raised in a barn?" she snaps. "Nice people don't use language like that."

"You mean the word 'pee?'" the nurse asks. She's trying hard not to laugh as my mother spits, "Darn right."

"What word do you use?"

"The proper word is 'urinate,'" Mom informs her primly, and the nurse smiles at her: "OK then, Vivian, would you like to urinate now?"

Mom rises laboriously, leaning on the nurse. "I'm ready to bust. No one even lets you go to the bathroom in this dump."

In the eight awful days that my mother spends in acute care, there is only one nurse I cannot respect. Kim is a chatty woman who is eager to make friends with me the first night she is on duty. When I try to introduce Mom as the sparkling, witty person she once was, Kim waves her hand and tells me that she already knows all that. Mom is still under heavy sedation at this point, pretty much

117

passive and numb. An easy case.

The second time Kim cares for my mother is an evening shift, six days into her stay on the unit. When I leave the hospital around six-thirty, my mother is fairly cheerful, telling Verna the same old stories about visiting her cousins on the farm in New Jersey. It is a Tuesday night, the swelling of Mom's forehead and face have gone down considerably, and I still hope that she'll be discharged before the weekend. By eight-thirty, however, I receive a distraught call from the nurse telling me that my mother is "completely out of control" and begging me to come in and calm her down. Imagining the worst, I try to phone Dr. Z as my husband drives me to the hospital.

Kim meets us outside Mom's room. Her face is flushed, her voice shrill and her hands shaking violently as she repeats what she said on the phone: "Your mother is completely out of control! I can't do anything for her. *You need to calm her down.*"

Inside the room, Mom is sitting on the edge of the bed shouting at Verna. There is a dinner tray overturned on the floor. People posing as nurses are trying to poison her, my mother screams, and she is not going to stand for it. They have stolen her shoes and her purse so she can't get away. They have kidnapped her husband so he can't rescue her. Verna is in cahoots with the so-called nurses. Her diatribe is liberally salted with growling, profanity and tears. Sadly, by this point, nothing about the scene strikes me as the least bit unusual.

My mother recognizes me as I walk in: "Judy, thank God you're here!" I sit beside her on the bed, hold her close. "It's alright now," I coo, "I'm here with you, and I'll never let anybody hurt you." Mom whimpers about the awful people, but she's running out of steam. I keep my voice low, rubbing her shoulders and neck. She leans heavily into my embrace. I help her to the toilet, wash her face, then coax her to take her evening medications (probably the trigger that started this whole scene in the first place).

My mother was one tough customer in the hospital. I could have forgiven Kim if she had admitted that she was out of her depth. Instead, as my husband and I are leaving, she waylays me to complain about Mom's bad behavior, warning that if there is any more trouble she will call for security. I apologize for her distress, explain again that my mother cannot help her delusions, and go home praying that we will make it through what's left of this nursing shift.

The following afternoon, Kim again is assigned to my mother. As soon as she comes on duty at 3PM, I take her aside: "I know that last night was very upsetting for you. Are you going to be alright with caring for my mother again? It's OK if you say no: Mom is hard to handle. We can arrange for somebody else. But I need to know right now whether or not you are up to this."

Kim does not make eye contact with me. Her hands fidget wildly. Yes, she assures me, she is absolutely fine with caring for my mother. She looks anything but fine. I repeat that no one will think less of her if she's not up to this, but she insists she can handle Mom's care, no problem. Up to this moment, I have done everything I can think of to foster good relationships with the nurses because I know they are having a difficult time with my mother; after a completely sleepless night, I call the director of nursing to insist that Kim never be assigned to care for her again.

Discharge Plans

Several proposed discharge dates come and go, yet Mom remains hospitalized. Dr. Y checks her daily, but defers to Dr. Z, the specialist, who recommends a few days of "de-tox" with little or no sedation so he can see how she is functioning: in this environment, "functioning" for my mother means cursing and fighting off ghosts, so every order he leaves that offers the nursing staff the option of sedation "as needed" is carried out to the max. Dr. Z wants to try a few different medications in sequence giving each one two to four days to see what calms her down: because Mom sleeps at erratic hours and the nurses are stretched so thin, she almost never receives a dose of medication at the time prescribed. More often than not, the "as needed" sedation is used to calm her down enough to give her whatever medication the doctor intended as a trial. Dr. Z is pressing to move Mom to the inpatient behavioral health unit, which he supervises: my father continues to resist.

As the first week wanes, Dr. Z and Dr. Y offer my father and me two options: since there is no longer any medical reason to keep Mom in acute care, she can either be discharged back to Cascia Hall, where she may or may not settle down, or she can be moved to the behavioral health unit, where Dr. Z will continue his efforts to stabilize her behavior. Both doctors strongly favor the latter option, and so do I. Only a few weeks ago, the mother of one of my friends was kicked out of a nursing home for slapping an aide; what if my mother is violent when she returns to Cascia Hall? My father is afraid to challenge the doctors, but he thinks they are overreacting to Mom's distress. Between his limited visiting privileges and my sins of omission, he believes she is doing pretty well. He has no idea of the depth of her paranoia, or that I return to the hospital every night to put out fires. Furthermore, in a miraculous example of the utility of short-term memory loss, my father claims to have forgotten the day we spent in the ER when she was first admitted. In deference to my father's wishes, plans are made to discharge my mother the following morning, barring a disaster.

The phone rings shortly before five A.M. As I reach to answer it, my husband stirs and mutters, "What a fucking nightmare." My mother is screaming so loudly I can hardly hear the nurse on duty, but I get the picture pretty quickly. I am out of bed and en route to the hospital so fast that I don't remember putting clothes on.

It's an aside, but important to say nonetheless: *I love my husband.* After thirty years of marriage I am still knocked speechless by his decency and his heart. I dare not speculate on how I found such a man, but I cherish the memory of him waking that morning, as we woke too many times during those awful weeks, to the phone ringing and another summons back to the hospital: he could have gone back to sleep, but instead he hugged me, saying, "I'll find my pants and come with you."

We hear Mom's voice the moment the elevator door opens, though we must be a hundred yards from her room. What all those other sick folks on the unit make of her shouting, I have no idea. You can pick out words now and then, or a vague notion of what or who she is she cursing, but mostly what I hear is that she has the volume cranked up to a higher level of terror than ever before.

As we jog past the nurses' station, I catch sight of a massive man in uniform rocking slowly back and forth in a swivel chair. He nods soberly as we race into Mom's room.

This is where my visual memory falters. I don't remember if she is standing, sitting on the bed, or lying in it. I don't remember who the nurse on duty is. I do remember that chaos prevails in the room, as if a major hailstorm is blowing through and my mother is the force behind the storm. She recognizes me, but howls right through my soothing words and smacks away my caresses. She is a force of nature, and we have no choice but to wait for her fury to blow over.

I hold in my mind a strange tableau from that morning. Verna is off to the right in shadow, discreet and loving as ever. The nurse, whoever she was, is to my left and behind me. Mom is slouched on

121

the bed, her hair wild and her hands gesturing in crazy loops, tearfully repeating, "You have no idea what they do to me here. You have no idea." Perched in a chair facing her, I am holding her arms to her sides and murmuring every reassuring phrase I have ever heard, whether or not it pertains to this scene. Behind me, my wonderful husband stands with his hand on my shoulder.

When Mom regains a measure of calm, when I have eased her back into bed and it looks like she might finally sleep, my husband and I head home. At the nurses' station, the security guard still rocks slowly, side to side, in his chair. "My mother has Alzheimer's," I say apologetically, "Please understand that she doesn't know what she's doing." He nods and shrugs. I want to ask him, "What would you have done if my mother had been strong enough to attack a nurse or an aide?" My husband grabs my elbow and steers me to the elevator.

By six-thirty A.M., I am home, and writing an email to my sister and the geriatric care consultant. It sets a new bar for understatement: "This probably means that plans to move her back to Cascia Hall today are scrapped."

However the nurses try to cover up an IV connection or a heart monitor, my mother worries at it with her fingers, exercising the peculiar fussiness of Alzheimer's: for years, she has been unable to see a cord without pulling it, to see a button without pressing it. With her arm wrapped in gauze and adhesive tape to protect the IV line, all her energy comes to bear on tugging, dislodging, removing. At some point, the nurses give up on the IV altogether for fear she will hurt herself pulling it out. Then they give up on the heart monitor, because she twists it into knots that leave painful red marks on her chest. Then – and this must violate hospital procedure – they give up on trying to keep the standard laminated ID bracelet on her wrist, because she pulls at and stretches it until it comes off. Eventually, although this is an acute care unit, nurses give up on taking her vital signs every few hours through the night.

There is one thing Mom never manages to pull off: a bright purple plastic bracelet on her left wrist. Though it must have been there from the start of her hospitalization, days pass before I notice it. It reminds me of the yellow "Live Strong" bracelets Lance Armstrong popularized to raise money for cancer research. Why is my mother wearing a doodad like this?

I try not to draw her attention to the band but, holding her hands in mine, I sneak a look. In bold white letters, the message on Mom's bracelet reads, "DNR."

My sister and close friends from childhood tease me for being a little slow on the uptake: sometimes, no matter how good the joke, I won't get it until someone's elbow jabs me hard in the ribs. My first thought, good Wisconsin gal that I am, is that my mother is wearing a bracelet from the Department of Natural Resources. But before that thought can settle into puzzlement, it dawns on me: in accordance with the living will she drew up fifteen years earlier, when she was of sound mind and a scenario like the one we are living was an unthinkable abstraction, the bracelet's message is "Do Not Resuscitate."

Talking quietly with my mother in the dimly lit room, I hold her wrist so that the bracelet is covered by my hand. It occurs to me that her hands are growing so skinny that I could slip it off and make it disappear like all the other bands and bandages. After all, she has already worked her way out of strictures that measure heartbeat and identity. Perhaps, shedding one more band, she could be free.

Then I finally get it: this is the band that sets her free.

III.

"… the images that rise unbidden are of my caring for my mother, just the two of us, cut off, isolated from the rest of the world."

-- Caterina Edwards, *Finding Rosa*

What Matters Most

More dreams about my mother last night. The details blur, as usual: I have some sort of appointment, and leave her in a waiting room with my daughter. I return to find her shrieking unintelligibly and, in an improbable effort to comfort her, straddle her lap and wrap my arms and legs around her. My words are echoes from the hospital near the end of her life – *Don't be frightened, Mom, I'm here. I won't let anyone hurt you. You're safe now, and I love you.* At some point, I rise, lift her in my arms, and hold her on my lap instead. At another moment, I become dimly aware that my daughter needs comforting, and extend my hand around behind my mother's back to her.

Then the setting shifts to a college where I keep misplacing my mother in various rooms while I rush around taking care of obligations, running late as always, stopping often to talk with people who really don't need my attention. Suddenly, the shock of becoming aware of the time, of realizing that she has been alone too long, and a terrified rush through crowded hallways calling for her. Someone beckons me into a pick-up truck to speed the search. An orange-robed Bengali woman steps up to the window and asks if we are looking for "the old lady sleeping in her undies." *Undies*, she says, a babyish word rendered ridiculous by her lilting sub-continental accent. (And why am I so sure she is Bengali?)

Mom is, of course, the old lady who, in a tantrum of fear, tore off her clothes and fussed herself to sleep in a pile of ragged blankets on a gym floor. "We could hear her shouting in Chicago," someone remarks, as several people work together to rouse her and settle her into the truck. Then a sequence of meaningless moves, dressing or undressing her, moving her in and out of the truck, every step the cause of more resistance on her part, and strangely true to my memories of caring for her at the end.

Many months after her death, my mother prowls the corridors of my sleep, trying every door; she wrings tears from my heart at unexpected moments. Sometimes she is small, a rag-doll hanging by her arms around my neck. Sometimes she is my baby, and sometimes she appears as the shadow woman, thin and depleted, she was at the moment she let go of life. The dreams are elusive, comforting, troubling, and often contain weird points of accuracy that mirror unwelcome truths. They remind me that I am usually looking outwards to avoid looking inwards; that I am giving so much to strangers that I avoid connection with those closest to me; that I am bossing everyone around, the ultimate parent, pretending that I know best for others when I am completely at sea myself.

She always had a way of pointing out what mattered most.

"I Didn't Say That," and Beyond

At last Dr. Z convinced my father that it was best to move Mom to the inpatient behavioral health unit. He assured us that she would receive more individual attention there and more therapeutic interactions, and that he would be able to supervise her care more closely. Even mealtimes would be more flexible. Besides, we had exhausted all other options at the hospital. Only one bureaucratic obstacle remained: never mind that my mother had no idea where she was or what was happening to her, and that my father and I had power of attorney for her healthcare – the hospital social worker informed me that the patient's own signature was legally required on a form.

The nurse on duty that Friday morning was a sympathetic woman who had taken the time to get my mother out of bed, to raise the blinds and admit natural light. As a result, Mom was in an upbeat mood when I arrived to feed her breakfast. She sat in the blue vinyl recliner before the windows, calm enough for once that the chair alarm was silent, immersed in conversation with someone who wasn't there.

"Hi, Mom." I leaned over to kiss her.

"Excuse me for a moment," she said to the empty space to the right of her chair.

"Who are you talking to?"

"This nice young lady. Do you have to interrupt?"

"I just want to visit with you, Mom. Shall we have some breakfast?"

She turned to the right again, extending her hand warmly, patting the air. "I'm sorry, Dear," she said, "this is my nosy daughter. I'll get back to you as soon as she leaves."

At that moment the social worker rapped at the door, handed me a sheaf of paperwork and a pen, and made it clear that she needed the signature in pretty short order.

Because my mother seemed calm and compliant, I tried a fairly direct approach first. "Mom, you've always had beautiful

129

handwriting. Write your name for me right here so I can see how you do it."

No dice. "What is this paper? They're trying to get all my money. You're trying to get me to sign something for them, and I won't do it."

I changed the subject, persuaded her to eat a few bites of cheerios and take a sip of coffee, brushed her hair. The social worker checked in, a little brusquely. I asked for more time. A few minutes later my mother drifted into a reverie in which she was shopping. "What would you like to buy, Mom?" I asked.

"A hat. With gardenias." I had to smile: that reference goes back to her days as a salesgirl at B. Altman's in the forties, selling elegant hats to rich women with a co-worker who charmingly called the flowers "Goddamnyas."

"Here's the credit card slip. Sign your name and it's yours."

"No," she said, "I don't like the way it looks on me." She didn't even bother to open her eyes. We were both playing games and I was losing.

"Write your name for me, Mom."

"Nope. Leave me alone."

The social worker thumped on the door again and I stepped out to explain that Mom did not seem inclined to sign anything, regardless of how it was presented. She fixed me with an exasperated glare. "When you close the door," she said, "nobody can see who signs the paper. And if anyone asks you, I didn't say that." Then she pressed the papers back into my hands and stalked away.

I did as I was told. I believed what I was told. Besides, there was no point in keeping Mom in acute care any longer. My mother was sitting right beside me as I forged her signature. She never opened her eyes and would not have thought to challenge me if she had. A moment later, I opened the door and handed the papers back.

A particularly perky nurse accompanied us down to the psychiatric unit an hour or so later. In my mother's eight days on the acute care floor this nurse had never been responsible for Mom, but she had heard the shouting and seen me coming and going at improbable hours, despite the presence of a hired caregiver overnight. She'd enjoyed her share of the bagels, brownies, and other goodies I regularly dropped off in the nurses' break room to show appreciation and foster goodwill towards my frightened, cantankerous mother. And, no doubt, she had heard the complaints of her colleagues about the impossible burden this one patient imposed.

I liked this woman. A lot. Though she never cared for Mom, she made a point of finding small ways to care for me. One early morning, after a full night of running back and forth to put out fires at the hospital, as I was racing to my mother's room, dressed in yesterday's clothes and with my hair a mess, she caught me in a hug, handed me a cup of coffee, and said, "You're doing a wonderful job."

I was very glad to have her pushing my mother's wheelchair now, though the trip from one floor to another seemed like a metaphor for Mom's time at Morana Hospital to date: because the new hospital had opened its doors only a couple of weeks before her fall, we kept hitting dead ends, ringing for inoperable elevators, passing through doors that should have been locked but, because they weren't, gave us access to private scenes of physical and emotional pain that were none of our business. My mother, in high spirits for the moment, remained unfazed. The sun shone bravely outside the infrequent windows we passed. The nurse smiled at me and said, "Hang in there, girlfriend."

Arriving at the behavioral health unit, the discomfort of identifying ourselves before a video camera and passing through two sets of locked doors was mitigated somewhat by the good cheer of the personnel who greeted us inside. At Dr. Z's urging I had forbidden my father from coming to see Mom for a day or two as she was moved. My mother was distracted by an occupational therapist who invited her to share memories of motherhood and

131

needlework, and I was ushered into a tiny lounge to meet with a psychiatric nurse.

The nurse assigned to my mother was petite, blond, poised, smart, and beautiful. She was also, she informed me, working on a PhD in nursing with a focus on the care of Alzheimer's patients. After a week adrift in the hospital, I was overcome with relief. She held my hand as I told her about my brilliant mother, how Alzheimer's had rearranged her world, how scared and lost she was. I confided my frustration with the blind spots of some of the acute care nurses, my fear of Mom's growing paranoia. I drew deep comfort from opening up to her in this way: Mom was now in the hands of people who had more patience and more training, I thought; in this new environment we would see dramatic improvement.

I left the hospital in late afternoon, drove home to pick up my dogs, and headed off for a long-overdue walk at the dog-park. It was a chilly, rainy day at a time of year when each day seems dramatically shorter than the one before. But thanks to my dogs, I am accustomed to being outside in natural light regardless of the season. Boo and Curtis did what dogs do at the park: they chased mice in the long grass, dug holes, sniffed, and romped with friends. For that hour, life felt normal. I felt hopeful.

Driving home across the Hoan Bridge, my cell phone rang. I switched off *All Things Considered* to answer. A rather formal gentleman introduced himself as a psychiatric social worker on the staff of Morana Hospital. "I understand," he said, "that your mother was admitted to inpatient behavioral health today. I've just got a couple of questions."

I had not seen my husband for more than a few moments in the preceding week. I had not met my classes and was way behind with grading. I had hardly walked my dogs until this afternoon. I was pretty much fried. And once we got past the introductory questions regarding the nature of my mother's fall and her history with Alzheimer's prior to hospitalization, this very sympathetic-sounding social worker started asking me to reflect upon the outlook for her remaining time on earth.

It was already after sunset on a completely uncertain November day. He had no apparent agenda. I told him that Mom was changing, that she was losing ground fast. I told him how it hurt to see her hallucinating, lashing out at invisible enemies, cursing her loved ones, agonizing over imagined regrets. As I had with the young nurse a few hours earlier, I poured out my heart to this social worker. And then he delivered the kick to the gut: "Your mother is combative and violent. Around five P.M. she injured one of our nurses, who is now in the emergency room."

My mother. I apologized profusely, not knowing why. My poor mother. She didn't know better. She must be terrified. She never meant to hurt a soul. I couldn't stop the apologies, as if they could change anything for my mother. I promised him I'd be there in less than half an hour.

When my daughter and I arrived, both the work shift and the atmosphere on the unit had changed. The evening nurse was brusque and uninformative, and I thought I could read a hostile sub-text in every glance. In the corridor outside the half-closed door, she informed me that it had been necessary to sedate and restrain my mother in order to protect the staff. They had also brought in a special aide to feed Mom: it was not going well, she said, but I was welcome to help if I thought I could.

Sedate. Restrain. Having spoken the English language my whole life, I thought I knew what these simple words meant. What dementia does not suck into its cockeyed vortex, however, the reality of inappropriate hospitalization will. My mother's door opened and one of the two massive men who usually served as aides on the floor emerged, nodding to me as he passed. My daughter and I entered.

My mother was seated in one of those hospital recliners that discourage one from standing up, but this time she couldn't have risen if her life depended on it because she was bound by a pelvic restraint. Her hair was wild, her bathrobe hiked up around her hips, revealing the straps that held her to the chair. She was so heavily

133

drugged that she was unaware of the frumpy volunteer with teased-up hair poking spoonfuls of pot-roast into her mouth. She didn't chew or respond: the food just fell back out as she slumped impossibly far over the armrest, babbling. Although I had brought her granddaughter to visit, she couldn't respond to us because she was engaged with another group of children. Imaginary children.

"Look at the little ones," she slurred, as the volunteer aide gave up and left, "We should give them balloons!" I headed out to ask what in hell they had done to my mother.

Ten minutes later, I returned to find my daughter kneeling beside the recliner. Her hands were rounded as if holding a balloon, which expanded with each exaggerated puff of breath she blew into it. "Is it big enough, Grandma?" she asked, and when my mother said, "Yes," she made as if to tie the end and handed it off to an invisible child. "They're such sweet children. They're happy," Mom mumbled.

It suddenly occurred to me to go back to the nurse's station and ask when was the last time anyone took my mother to the toilet. The people behind the desk looked at one another in puzzlement, as if this was an alien concept: *To the toilet?* I had accompanied my mother to this floor around ten in the morning and it was now after six. In all that time, no one had thought to take her to the bathroom, though they had the presence of mind to *sedate* and *restrain* her *in order to protect the staff.* "She needs to go to the bathroom," I said, rather too loudly, as if this were news. "Someone will be with her in a few minutes," the nurse replied. After a long, traumatic day in an environment she could not comprehend, my mother was finally offered the chance to urinate, with two nurses and one of those gigantic aides in attendance to keep them safe. And me, because I didn't feel safe leaving her side.

My mother was now on a "behavioral health unit," where every aspect of her care was to be supervised by a geriatric psychiatrist. When I agreed to this move, I had not fully understood that legal guidelines for employing physical and pharmacological restraints to control patient behavior on a locked psychiatric unit are more flexible than elsewhere in a hospital. Mom could not have been bound to her bed or a chair on the acute care unit, but here all bets were off. Moreover, the notion of "advocacy" in this environment was pretty much moot: the doctor had authority, and his handpicked staff was an extension of his will. There was, in other words, not a lot that I could do about the state in which I found my mother that evening: if I regarded this treatment as upsetting, that was my problem. My only recourse would be to remove my mother from the hospital altogether, against all medical advice we had received.

The following morning, in another lame effort to foster good will towards my Mom, I approached the injured nurse to apologize and hear her side of the story. Apparently, she had tried to give my mother some pills and Mom resisted. When the nurse forced the issue, pressing the pills into Mom's hand, my mother grabbed her by the wrist and shouted, "No!"

Though it seemed ridiculously obvious, I set about explaining the incident. My mother was sundowning even before she fell: late in the day when she was tired, the lights were low and her poor eyesight made the shadows seem more ominous, she would grow increasingly agitated and scared. This was not an unusual pattern, and it was exacerbated by the fact that Mom had been badly injured, passed a traumatic week on one floor of the hospital, and had been moved yet again to an unfamiliar place. Surely a nurse who was working on a PhD with a focus on Alzheimer's care would understand.

That beautiful young woman with a brace on her wrist and an aspiration to work with dementia patients never met my gaze again, even when I spoke to her directly. And I made a point of speaking to her directly. "My wrist is sprained," she whined, cradling her right arm in her left as if it were made of porcelain.

Sundowning

August, 2011

The moon is full. A harvest moon, golden and low above Lake Michigan. Its candescence spills across the water, a path to the horizon and whatever lies beyond. Hours after sunset, I can still see my shadow cast on the sand, the hollows of my footprints. Its borrowed light is lovelier than sunshine, more nuanced and melancholy. It suits this night's reflections: I am no longer young; I've lost my mother. Now moonlight tugs my heart toward regret when I think of her last full moon, the moon that poured its wild light through the windows of Morana Hospital, its path away beginning at her door.

It is the summer after my mother's death. My elder dog Boo is probably thirteen by now; because she started life as a stray, there's no way to know for sure. If my guess at her age is correct, and if we calculate dog years with the traditional ratio of seven to one, she's like a person who's over ninety. In recent months she has begun to show signs of dementia: she forgets to eat, walks into the corner and gets stuck there, whines with frustration, reverses day and night. She is a dazed and dopey version of herself, sleeping while the sun is up and rising into a state of agitation as it sets. Most nights she wants to stay outside all night, lying on the back stoop, watching clouds blow past the moon. Boo seems happier in those moments than at any other time these days.

Just as day and night have reversed, Boo's desire to sleep outside is a complete flip of what she wanted when she first joined our family. Back then her most fervent hope was to come in out of the storm, to be as close to me as possible. Though we're pretty sure she lived with humans in her early life, it's likely she had not been allowed indoors. In the rainy north Georgia Mountains, perhaps the driest place she could find to sleep was under the eaves, waiting for the door to open in hopes of being fed in the morning. I wonder if Boo is reverting to puppyhood, sleeping outdoors because it is what she first knew and remembers most vividly, never mind that it may not be a happy memory or that she has long been able to call our quiet and secure house her home. Now she paces and pants, whines and cries, until I let her out. I lie awake waiting for her barked request to come in. It never seems to come.

The way I understand Boo's behavior is this: she's sundowning. "Sundowning," or increased confusion at the end of the day and into night, is a symptom common to people with dementia. While the cause is not known, it may be aggravated by fatigue, low lighting, gathering shadows and a disruption of the body's natural clock. Days of napping decline into nights of agitation. Anyone who's cared for a loved one with Alzheimer's will recognize the pattern.

My mother's sundowning began before we moved her to Cascia Hall. She would stay in bed most of the day, resist my father's efforts to rouse or dress or feed her, and suddenly come awake with a paranoid vengeance as the sun went down. By that time, Dad would have ordered their dinner to be brought up from the dining room, and she would refuse to eat it. She would call him a terrible husband and sometimes throw the food on the floor. If I rushed to the rescue, bringing in a home-cooked meal and feeding it to her (still in her nightgown from the night before), she might deign to eat a few bites. Eventually I would leave because my father insisted that he needed no help. I still can't stand to think about what he must have gone through in his efforts to put her to bed.

Not surprisingly, this pattern increased with the move to Cascia Hall. The first night Mom spent there, she refused to go to bed until three A.M. (I gather this is not an unusual story). The next morning, however, the staff was able to get her up and dressed, and my sister witnessed her happily playing Bingo, something she would never have done had she been aware of what she was doing. It seemed we were on a roll.

But nothing is predictable with Alzheimer's, except the guarantee that you will always lose more ground, and professional advice could not derail my father's obsessive need to continue putting his wife to bed. Seven P.M. would find him stumbling down the nursing home hall to her room, where she would first act flirtatious then throw him out, threaten to divorce him then make lavish declarations of love. "Norman, why won't you sleep with me?" she'd whine. He was at a loss for how to answer.

In the hospital, my mother's sundowning escalated wildly. Since she kept her eyes closed and the blinds drawn, whether it was light or dark outside was beside the point. Early in the day she could reminisce about her cousins' farm in New Jersey, her sorority sisters, even graduate school on a really good day. She could sing and I could make her laugh with stupid jokes remembered from childhood. But as twilight gathered and an increasingly full moon rose over the lake outside, dangerous people clustered in the shadows, sneering and plotting, growling threats at her.

The nursing home social worker and the geriatric care consultant both expressed their belief that the full moon has an unexplained power over Alzheimer's patients. My father would call this unscientific claptrap, and he may be right: most studies of lunar effects on human behavior fail to demonstrate a clear correspondence. But a few credible studies support the notion that individuals with Alzheimer's exhibit more volatile behaviors during periods of the full moon. I'm no scientist, but this makes sense to me. The moon has more power than the sun to influence tides, and the human brain is about seventy-five percent water. Transformation tales about werewolves at the full moon evoke the supernatural, but all-too natural patterns of mental illness are called "lunacy." The full moon blurs the border between light and darkness; the language deriving from it blurs the border between observation and myth.

Eight months after Mom's death, my sweet old Boo is sundowning under the full moon she longs to sleep beneath, and I can't seem to rest. My heart frets and paces in fear of something worse and more ineffable than coyotes, dognappers or lightning: the cold, staring fact that she is losing herself, that soon I will lose my dear companion. I rise in the night and stand at the window, trying to make out her black form in the darkness. Even the moonlight fails to help me keep her.

When I cleaned out my mother's room, I found notes kept by Verna during all those dark hours of sitting with my mother at the hospital. In nearly every entry Verna noted that Mom became more and more agitated as the sun set. But somehow, in her formal, laborious penmanship, Verna spelled out the wrong word. "Vivian became *adjudicated* when night nurse came in," she wrote. Or, "Bedtime = more *adjudication*." It was the kind of error I routinely see when my students place too much faith in spell check. Here was Verna, though, writing in long-hand in a dim hospital room, with no dictionary and no computer, just her own flawed education, her generous heart, and her inner spell check tuned to the injustice that night was falling for my mother in this unforgiving place.

Behavioral Health

The first night Mom spent on the locked unit, I phoned the nurses' station to check on her. I'd been given all the *pro forma* reassurances, of course: that it was fine to call at any time, day or night, whenever I wanted an update. Unable to sleep, I placed the call at two A.M. A rather dismissive male nurse told me she continued to be difficult through the evening and had been sedated again. What medications had she been given and when? He couldn't say. When had she gone to sleep? He couldn't say. I started to enumerate my concerns, that she was frightened and disoriented, that the reason for moving her to the behavioral health unit was to regularize the administration of her medications... clearly, I was talking too much for him. "We've had several admissions today and we're short-staffed," he snapped, "so there's no point in you asking for all these details. Why don't you just call back tomorrow?"

Before Mom's move, Dr. Z extolled the benefits of having my mother in the care of his own staff. He referred to them as "my people," and I envisioned a crackerjack team of quality nurses and occupational therapists who functioned in seamless support of patients. Even at first glance, the staff on the locked unit was dramatically different from the gentle, harried female nurses and aides in acute care. In addition to the fact that most of the nursing staff was male, there was a constant crowd of personnel, who I supposed to be therapists of different types, bustling about the nursing station in street clothes. (After one initial conversation with an occupational therapist, none of these people ever interacted with my mother or me again.) And then there were the aides: every shift had at least one male aide in attendance, hired, apparently, on the basis of size and unsmiling demeanor. These men were towering, glowering, broad-shouldered, deep-voiced, and clearly capable of pinning down anyone who got out of hand. They were such an intimidating presence that it took me a few days to figure out that the aides were gentle and genial souls who approached my mother with tenderness.

The nurse assigned to my mother the first morning she woke up on the locked ward was a short, balding man named Kevin. It wasn't so much his taciturn manner that worried me at first: it was the very fact that he was male. My father would have a fit, I thought, and my mother would refuse to cooperate. How was a strange man supposed to help her to the toilet, to bathe her, to dress her? Clearly, I'd have to take care of everything myself.

Kevin had other ideas, and he politely asked me to sit in the lounge down the hall while he got Mom up and ready for the day. "Are you sure?" I asked. He waved me away.

I wandered off to the lounge where yesterday I had met with the petite blonde nurse who raised and then dashed my hopes. Settling down at a table, I took out my notebook and began drafting the day's to-do list: calls to the geriatric care consultant, the eldercare agency, the Cascia Hall social worker. More calls to my office, to arrange for a sub to meet my classes, to apologize to advisees I had neglected, to postpone meetings and appointments. In shuffled a trembling young man in hospital pajamas. "Can I be here?" he asked tentatively. I told him that I was just sitting down for a few minutes, and it was OK with me if he stayed. He perched expectantly on an orange vinyl chair to my left, eyes fixed on my face. "Are you here, too?"

So here I was, at eight A.M. on the locked psych ward, in this ugly lounge furnished with orange and aqua vinyl, in a hospital where every other lounge was tastefully done in natural wood and tweed, and this poor guy posing his existential question, "Are you here, too?" "I'm visiting my mother," I told him, and he nodded thoughtfully. It looked like he was rehearsing in his mind whatever he would say next. Before he could speak, the door swung open and an officious woman in a tailored pink suit burst in: "You can't be here," she said, her words echoing my companion's. "We have a group scheduled in this room. You need to leave right now." The young man cast me a terrified glance as he headed for the door.

With nowhere else to sit, I returned to Mom's room. As I hesitated outside her half-closed door, I heard laughter and the comforting sound of conversation. I peeked in to see my mother seated on the edge of the bed, her nightgown pulled up around her waist, and Kevin kneeling on the floor before her easing her feet one at a time into the legs of a clean pair of panties. They were talking about Flushing, the part of Queens where my mother had spent most of her childhood. He made a childlike potty-joke about the name's connotations, and Mom cheerfully informed him, "It's Dutch. They have lots of funny words. Even 'kill' is a place."

Kevin was a wonder. He was as shocked as I was at how bad my mother smelled after her first week in the hospital, and somehow he persuaded her to let him give her a thorough sponge bath. He got her to bend over so he could spray her bottom with lotion that would protect her thinning skin against sores. He could do everything except help put on her bra: "Can you handle this?" he asked me, "I've never understood how these things work." He kept Mom talking, kept her happy, got her up to walk the corridors and look outside at Lake Michigan, sneaked food into the conversation and persuaded her to eat a little bit… for one amazing eight-hour shift, I felt my burden lighten. Kevin could reach Mom and he seemed to love her.

Kevin's shift ended in late afternoon. That evening, Mom fell apart again, refusing to eat or take her pills. The evening nurse injected her with the maximum meds allowed. By morning, when Kevin came on again, we were back where we started, with no regular program of medication in place, and no sense of what might help to stabilize her.

Stories That Break My Heart

Two octogenarians meet in a nursing home, where their loving families have placed them out of necessity. One started life as a burly mid-western farm kid who grew to be a star wrestler. By chance and a good bit of luck, he gained a measure of fame in the early days of pro-wrestling, taking on Killer Kowalski and "Da Crusher," and donating a significant portion of his winnings to charity. The other is a Holocaust survivor who overcame the horrors of his youth and went on to become a distinguished cancer researcher. He is also a concert violinist and founder of a Unitarian congregation.

These are old and decent men. Both suffer from Alzheimer's, and this takes a toll on their families. The wrestler is cared for by his children; the scientist/musician by his wife.

There are parts of this story that no one can tell, because no one notices what trivial altercation in the dining room begins it. The former pro-wrestler body slams the scientist, who falls and breaks his hip. Two weeks later, he is dead.

The death is ruled a homicide. *Homicide* means the killing of a human being, which is a true description of the act. It is also one of the most loaded words in the language, implying intention and the need for retribution. But this death begs deeper questions: What does intention mean for a person with dementia? Can we presume to understand who or what it was this old guy meant to knock down? What kind of retribution can society exact from someone who has lost everything already, including his past and his identity?

This happened in Minnesota in 2009: in a momentary conflict in a nursing home called Friendship Village, Verne Gagne, eighty-two, caused the death of Helmut Gutmann, ninety-seven. Even the victim's wife said, "You can't blame the person that did it... (he) doesn't know what he is doing. I feel so sorry for his family, because they are faced with a terrible problem of what to do." Because death is the natural end of life, I have always resisted the custom of routinely calling every death "tragic." Death is sad for the living, but death often makes sense; sometimes it's even a blessing. Though I'd be willing to wager that neither Gagne nor Gutmann had much longer to live, and that neither regularly recognized his loved ones anymore, this death strikes me as a uniquely tragic event.

The saddest aspect of this story is its ordinariness. Alzheimer's victims are often prone to outbursts of violence. A person of great dignity and composure is suddenly defeated by daily tasks. A person who is accustomed to being competent and capable is suddenly unable to function in the simplest situations. Reality shape-shifts, awareness flows back and forth in time, layers of memory smear like finger-paints, and nothing makes sense: who would not feel desperate? My mother's father knocked his wife flat on the kitchen floor. My husband's uncle bloodied the nose of a neighbor in the nursing home. My husband's grandfather chased a group of children off his property with an axe. These were good men, men of intelligence and heart. At some point, though, Alzheimer's led them to stumble across an ill-defined border between familiar and unfamiliar, oriented and disoriented. All the rules by which they had lived their lives were suddenly up for grabs.

I imagine my mother's brain near the end of her life looking something like my father's desk looks now: a clutter of documents that no one can identify, slips of paper with passwords that unlock nothing, a whirlwind of junk mail and unpaid bills mixed in with personal notes and family photos. When a person can no longer make sense of the information stacked up in the mind, when everything jumbles and swirls and you can't trust anyone else's attempts to organize it for you, the world must seem a profoundly dangerous place.

In 2010, in my hometown of Milwaukee, a man named Richard Petersen became combative in the seniors' residence where he lived with his wife of fifty-nine years. Petersen and his wife apparently had some important things in common with my parents: the length and stability of their marriage, the thought and preparation that they had given to their care at the end of life, the fact that one partner developed Alzheimer's, and the support and loyalty of their grown children. I can't help thinking that my mother would have liked Richard Petersen, a gregarious milkman who ran a boarding kennel for dogs while raising four daughters. Because my parents had looked at an apartment in the same facility where the Petersens lived, it's hard not to follow this line of thinking into the fact that they might have been neighbors.

When Richard Petersen's dementia reached the point where he was lashing out violently, police were called to the retirement home. Petersen was shuttled between two or three hospitals, depending upon which news account you read (including the hospital where my mother spent sixteen days; at the time, reportedly, no bed was available for him on the inpatient behavioral health unit). Finally, for want of anywhere else to take him, he was committed to the county psychiatric hospital, "where his family said they found him tied in a wheelchair with no jacket and no shoes... 'Nobody wants our dad,' said one of his daughters."

Though Alzheimer's is a medical illness, not a psychiatric condition, there are not many places in the current health care system for a dementia patient whose behavior becomes dangerously volatile. According to another of Petersen's daughters, the police, lacking other options, placed her father under "Emergency Detention, Chapter 51.15." "Under the statute, he could be taken into custody if police thought he was mentally ill with a 'substantial probability' of causing harm to himself or others." As Petersen's daughters worked unsuccessfully to secure his release from the county mental health facility, their father contracted pneumonia and died within hours of his transfer to Froedtert Hospital.

In the words of Tom Hlavacek, executive director of the Alzheimer's Association of Southeastern Wisconsin, "an estimated 100,000 people in Wisconsin have Alzheimer's and the number is expected to hit 130,000 by 2025." Average life expectancy in Wisconsin is 77.9 years, which places the state roughly tenth on a national scale. Because the Petersen family went public with their painful experience, an Alzheimer's task force was convened in Milwaukee to "seek better care for those who become aggressive."

"This is the greatest generation," Hlavacek was quoted in the Milwaukee Journal-Sentinel, "they have survived the depression, fought WWII, and here is what we give them. It's a crying shame we can't do better by our older adults." An article dated December 7, 2010 – the day of my mother's death – opens with this sentence: "Milwaukee police were dispatched more than 380 times to nursing homes during the first six months of 2010, a figure that shocked even those activists and officials who deal with older adults."

In the same article, Chapter 51 admissions are described as being "symptomatic of a broken system, often leading to treatment that includes 'the involuntary administration of psychotropic drugs to reduce agitation and aggression and produce a state of sedation.'"

Richard Petersen's daughters appear to be smart and competent women. They clearly did their best to care for their parents under adverse circumstances. Arguably, they had everything a family could hope for: resources, education, emotional support, money, and love. But there is no happy ending to this story: they did not succeed in bringing their father home from a hospital where he should never have been placed. Petersen died alone, among strangers. His unintended legacy may be a wake-up call to other families: though it's important to be an advocate for your loved ones, advocacy may not be enough when nursing homes, hospitals, and all the "experts" are ill-equipped to care for an elder with Alzheimer's.

I learned about both of these cases by following them on the internet, which means that I also had the opportunity to follow the crass commentary that tends to accumulate online in this age of no accountability. There were thirty postings the first time I checked in on responses to coverage of Richard Petersen's story in the Milwaukee Journal-Sentinel: fourteen expressed support and commiseration for the family; sixteen ranted against "Obama-care" and/or blamed the family for being whiners. There were fewer responses on the site where I first read the Gagne-Gutmann story, but they were merciless: "There is nothing I could possibly add to this story that would make it funnier." "Without assistance from anybody on the internet, this story has supplanted itself (sic) as the funniest story in the history of mankind." "Fucking HIL-ARIOUS!"

"You just can't make this stuff up," crowed one of the online responders. He's got a point. In the end, Alzheimer's is the cruelest joke, even more unfair than the mocking remarks of unaccountable fools. After living long and meaningful lives, Verne Gagne, Helmut Gutmann, Richard Petersen, my husband's grandfather and uncle, my grandparents, my mother, and countless others end their days in confusion and torment. What I would wish upon those who find their misery "fucking hilarious" is a long, hard look in the mirror.

"This Should Not Be Our Problem"

Two days after my mother sent that pretty nurse to the ER with a sprained wrist, I had a meeting with Dr. Z. I was anxious to know whether or not he saw behavioral improvement with medication, and how he regarded Mom's prognosis for discharge from the hospital. I brought along the independent geriatric care consultant, whom I had come to regard as a trusted guide and advocate. Dr. Z, I was to learn, resented what he saw as the intrusion of this woman. Up to that point, I had persuaded myself that Dr. Z and I had an acceptable level of communication. I had tolerated his impatience with my father, whose anxiety was exhausting even for me: after all, who could withstand the repetition, the selective hearing, the wishful litany of questions that presupposed a hopeful answer no one could provide? I excused Dr. Z's manner because, as a geriatric psychiatrist, I imagined that he had deep, compassionate insight into my mother's situation. Perhaps, I rationalized, he's simply overworked; perhaps he's just having a bad day. I overlooked the fact that his area of specialization should have made him a sympathetic and respectful listener to my father as well.

Midway through the meeting, Dr. Z took a call. After exchanging a few words with the caller, he turned on the speaker so we could hear both sides of the conversation. It seemed that an ambulance had just delivered an elderly woman with dementia to the ER at Morana. She was not ill or injured: the ambulance had been called and she was taken to the hospital because, in a moment of agitation, she had swung her cane at a staff person at the retirement community where she lived. With characteristic brusqueness, Dr. Z agreed to come down to see the patient later, then ended the call and turned to us. "See what we have to deal with all the time? Some old lady tries to hit somebody with her cane and she ends up at the hospital. This should not be our problem, but the nursing homes send people here when they don't want to deal with them."

"My mother came to the hospital because she fell and hit her head," I reminded him.

Dr. Z countered that my mother's fall was the reason why she was admitted, but the reason why she was still there ten days later was because she so easily became combative. He repeated, as though we had any illusions, that Alzheimer's is an incurable disease, posing the same irritable questions he'd posed in every conversation I could remember: Did we expect him to work miracles? Did we simply want him to fill her up with drugs? The geriatric care consultant, in her measured voice, suggested that what we wanted was a way to return Mom to Cascia Hall safely, which implied attempting to stabilize her behavior. Dr. Z rolled his eyes and groaned.

During Mom's hospitalization Dr. Z reminded my father and me of the incurability of Alzheimer's so often that I began to question: What *did* I want? I didn't want a cure. Or, to be more accurate, *I desperately wanted a cure*, but since I knew better than to indulge that dream, I wanted a way to care for her effectively. At times I thought I wanted her to be like some of the other old people at Cascia Hall, the ones who placidly shuffled out of their rooms and sat silently before the TV all day. Though they moved like automatons, they didn't seem to share my mother's terror. Because my mother was relatively cheerful before her fall, I hadn't fully assimilated the fact that other dementia patients were probably being treated with the same powerful psychotropic drugs that Dr. Z was now trying with her. If I wanted doctors to find a way to relieve Mom's fear and panic, so that in whatever time she had left she would be calm enough to receive our love and care, the risk was that *pharmacological restraints* would become our new normal.

In retrospect, much of Mom's paranoia had a strange coherence to it. Whether responding to the hospital environment or referring to Cascia Hall (which she called "that place" or "that other place"), she frequently warned me, "These are dangerous people. They do terrible things to old ladies." At times her descriptions of beatings and torture became unbearably graphic, but at other times they

149

seemed almost recognizable. When she told me, "They tie old people up and poke holes in them; you can't imagine the screaming," I couldn't help wondering how daily nursing functions must appear to her in her diminished state. One old man at Cascia Hall was tied into his wheelchair to keep him from falling out; it took two aides to lift him, roaring, in or out of the chair, and as often as not his pants would fall down around his ankles in the process. There was an old woman who spent most of every day screaming that no one would let her go to the bathroom, though aides took her to the toilet every hour or two, and another who wept continuously. Her neighbors unwillingly choked down pills, received injections, and suffered delusions of their own. None of these people was being neglected or mistreated, but my loving mother felt their pain as her own.

Behind Locked Doors

I heard Jane Gross, author of *A Bittersweet Season,* speaking on NPR about caregiving for elders. "It kicks up all the dust of childhood," she said, meaning that adult siblings caught up in care giving can occasionally be reduced to who they were at ten years old, when "all the fights boil down to 'Mommy loved you more than she loved me.'"

Thanksgiving is a holiday precious to my family. Besides its bracingly secular nature and our shared love of good food, my parents married the day before Thanksgiving, 1951, so that the holiday weekend might stand in for the honeymoon they couldn't afford. My brother-in-law and niece have late November birthdays. When Hanukkah comes early, it's closer to Thanksgiving than to Christmas, and when it comes late we celebrate it early anyways because we seldom manage to gather the whole family in December. In 2010 my mother spent the week before Thanksgiving on the behavioral health unit, and at every visit I reminded her that Maura, my older sister, would be here soon.

One day, when I returned from fetching my father, I paused to listen at my mother's door, trying to gauge what scene we were about to enter. Instinctively, I blocked Dad's access, in case something might be upsetting. But this time, I heard pleasant voices: Kevin, the best nurse on the unit, was asking Mom about her children, and she was describing my sister as I slipped into the room. "I'm back Mom!"

"Maura?" my mother cried, "Where's Maura? Where's Maura?" Her hands searched the air around her recliner like a blind person feeling for a misplaced object.

"Maura won't be here for a few days yet. It's me, Judy."

My mother turned to Kevin and grunted. "I thought Maura was here, but it's only Judy. Judy's good for nothing."

After Mom's death, my sister rediscovered a twenty-year-old video clip shot at our family's cottage on Cape Cod. At the time it was filmed, our mother was sixty-something and retired, filling her days with volunteering and needlework, lunching with friends, planning overseas holidays for herself and my father, visiting her far-flung grandchildren. She wears a summer blouse and blue culottes, and her greying hair is permed to frame her face with curls. Her glasses, which must have been stylish at the time, have lenses the size of drink coasters. As the film rolls, she leads her grandkids in the kind of pre-school story hour she presented once a week at the Carnegie Library near their house in Pittsburgh. The audience consists of three young mothers – my sister, me, and the daughter of our mother's best friend – plus six children, two to a mother, ranging from infancy to six years old.

My mother appears a little frazzled in the video, as if suffering from stage fright. She fumbles for words, misreads some phrases. When she garbles a simple song, her friend's grandson corrects her. Her cheeks flush with the effort of ensuring that the children have fun, that they learn, that they share in a perfect experience.

Her best friend's grandkids are the ideal audience: cute, smart, attentive, calling out whatever responses Mom invites. My sister's older daughter also listens well, laughing her adorable machine-gun laugh at the all the right moments, while the younger daughter contentedly sucks at a bottle. My own children, ages four and two, follow agendas of their own: my daughter sprawls amid a herd of tiny plastic horses, moving them here and there, whispering to herself the vivid tales of their lives; my son investigates his environment like a detective, flicking a light switch on and off, crawling under a chair to see how it's put together, studying the movement of clouds outside the picture window. I am certain that both are keeping up with Mom's story, noting the slow progression of images as the pages, facing outward toward the listeners, turn and turn again, but their concentration strays.

And what of the young mothers in this film? Slimmer, prettier versions of the women we are today, we also play to type. Kathy, lifelong friend to my sister and me, watches from a slight remove, the dramatic shawl of her hair framing a quiet smile. Maura sits cross-legged on the floor, cradling her younger daughter, leaning forward now and then to murmur encouragement to the elder. I am a blur of nervous energy – retrieving my son from this or that momentary exploration, redirecting my daughter from her inner story, laughing too loud at my mother's jokes, pushing my children to deliver the appearance of undivided attention to her.

The picture book bobbles awkwardly in my mother's hands and she crinkles a page. She is having trouble reading upside down, but she is trying so hard. Watching this footage, I am startled to see how my mother and I mirror one another, bound by an un-severed cord between her anxiety about whether or not she measures up, and my own.

Strange as it seems, my mother and I had some good times in her first few days on the locked ward, and I regret that, because I restricted his access, Dad didn't get to share them. Kevin consistently worked the day shift, and he managed to keep Mom's spirits up, to keep her walking the corridors, to keep me hoping that she would rally and return. He tended to her comfort meticulously, and she would do almost anything for him, including making the effort to occasionally open her eyes.

Near the end of his shift one day, Kevin helped me to guide Mom on a walk around the unit then left us settled into chairs in a lounge overlooking Lake Michigan. It was a gloomy afternoon with storm clouds massing over the face of the lake. Just a glimpse of the open air and water beyond buildings across the street seemed to bring my mother a measure of peace. We sat quietly, holding hands. I asked Mom if there was anything she wanted at the moment, and she replied, "A story."

"What kind of a story?"

"You know. Tell me a story."

Caught off guard, my mind went blank. I studied the wind-tossed trees around the old stone water tower that rises like fairy tale castle kitty-corner from the hospital. "A story," my mother barked, shaking my hand with impatience. It seemed miraculous, in that moment, that she could keep her focus, that she knew what she wanted. Pointing out the window, I told her the first story that popped into my head: when my friend Julie was a child, she was convinced that she'd been born at the top of the water tower. Every time they drove down the lakefront, her parents made a habit of gesturing up the hill toward Morana Hospital and saying, "You were born up there!" Because the tower stood between the lakeshore drive and the hospital, Julie got the location wrong. With my mother's passion for understanding how children viewed the world, this was a story she would have enjoyed earlier in life, but she couldn't follow the narrative anymore. I told her it was funny. She smiled vaguely. At last she grew tired. One of the immense aides came to help me steer her back to her room.

The next morning, I arrived to find that Kevin was no longer caring for her. We never saw him again.

Lonnie, the new day nurse assigned to my mother, was everything Kevin was not: rigid, judgmental, and wedded to convenience. If Mom ignored his first ultimatum to get up and greet the day, he gave her more medication and let her languish until afternoon. If she resisted going to the bathroom in his presence, he shrugged and left her in bed. If she was disinclined to eat, he set the tray aside and went back to his paperwork. If I suggested that we might do better at getting Mom up and engaged, he became defensive and dug in his heels. If Mom was to get out of bed, to eat, to bathe, to interact, it was my job and mine alone. But I had no control over her meds.

The hope that Kevin's care had instilled in me faltered. When Lonnie took over the day shift, Mom's activity level dropped below where it had been even on the acute care unit. "Nursing" was reduced to administration of medications, with minimal interaction.

I continued coming in at eight and staying until around four, with quick run-outs to fetch my father at noon and bring him home at two. It wasn't easy to lay low during Dad's visits with Mom, but I tried: he had known her through so many stages of her life that he couldn't stop talking to the person she had been. His over-explaining drove me crazy. Her confusion about where and who she was led to fruitless discussions of an injury she could not remember ("You fell and hit your head." "The hell I did! You've been brainwashed. They took out my mind, and I was screaming"). His efforts to feed her lunch turned into lengthy lectures about nutrition ("You need to eat a balanced diet." "That's poisoned! Take it away. Why don't you eat it and die"). Her anxiety about going home inspired him to rhapsodize about homes she no longer remembered ("In the house on Bellerock Street..." "I live at 11-07 160th Street in Flushing"). I dreaded leaving my parents alone together.

On Lonnie's shifts, Mom mostly sat in her room by herself, and anything I brought in to entertain her caused problems. The photographs of her parents and her grandchildren were unacceptable because there was glass in the frames. The iPod we'd stocked with familiar old songs, which Kevin had happily left playing all afternoon, was unacceptable because it had a cord. Nobody spoke to me about these concerns, they simply waited until I left, then confiscated the offending objects. I understand, of course, the ethos of a locked psychiatric ward and the need to protect vulnerable patients, but I still find it hard to imagine what was gained by depriving a sad old lady of family photographs and familiar songs.

With the switch from Kevin to Lonnie, my mother's behavior took a turn for the worse. For a few days, I had dared to think there was a pattern taking shape – fairly tranquil days, followed by anxious evenings – and the prospect of return to Cascia Hall seemed to be within reach again. But now the late shift also changed, and we were back to the unsympathetic nurse who took my call on Mom's first night on the behavioral health unit. After two weeks of hospitalization and a raft of psychotropic drugs, it seemed that we were barely treading water.

The Long Way Home

It freezes my heart to think about the prevalence of Alzheimer's in my mother's family. The disease has a terrible potency, and there are genetic risk factors. It doesn't just gum up the works in a human brain: it wreaks havoc with time itself. The past splits open, memory bleeds into confabulation; the present exists as a disjointed string of moments lacking any logical progression that might make meaning of events. The future is reduced to irrelevance. Because, barring great medical breakthroughs, chances are good that I will follow in my mother's footsteps, to share her unquiet fate, I have given much thought to what was going on in her mind as she lost herself to dementia. The closest I can come to imagining the confusion of her psyche is to revisit states of troubled dreaming: certain places and faces are recognizable, but everything is fluid. Objects and people juxtapose without boundaries, identity morphs and shifts, locations flow. Even the point of view of the dreamer is not a trustworthy constant.

As the second Monday of Mom's hospitalization dawned, I had no choice but to face the degree to which my role as caretaker was wreaking havoc with my own sense of time. Had I really, for the most part, been absent from my job and my family for nearly two weeks? Depending upon the moment, it either felt like, my mother had just fallen, or it felt like life had always followed this desperate rhythm and always would. Though I clung to my hope that she would soon be released from the hospital, it was growing harder and harder to imagine being anywhere but here.

Among many dozens of emails I sent that week, a handful managed to survive my disorganization. If their content could be plotted as a bar graph, the bottom axis would represent the passage of days at Morana Hospital, with double columns rising to measure the ratio of hope to disappointment. Disappointment always stands up taller. After a reasonably calm Monday, for example, I called the hospital, then sent this message to my sister and the geriatric care consultant:

9:25 PM –

Sorry, you two. Apparently, Mom had a bad spell again this evening, and when the nurse tried to help, Mom swung her walker and hit her in the face. Knocked her glasses off. Nurse says she's OK, but Mom received extra sedation (again), and is now in bed but not sleeping.

Dad is obsessing about meeting w/Dr. Z tomorrow, though I can't imagine what the Dr. can say at this point, and you know how I feel about his charming manner.... I had hoped to protect Dad from the knowledge that Mom sent a nurse to the ER the other day, but I guess the jig is up.

The following morning, my father and I had a lengthy meeting with Dr. Z. Dad's anxiety level, coupled with his own cognitive limitations, made for a dizzying circular conversation that clearly tested the doctor's patience. Knowing how little my father would retain, I emailed him that evening with a recap: I repeated Dr. Z's current plan for Mom's medication, tentative discharge date, and care recommendations that would accompany her return to Cascia Hall, including his customary advice that family members minimize our visits. Most of what I took from this meeting was the same old same old stuff, but Dr. Z clearly explained a couple of points that my father needed to grasp: my mother, he stated, must hereafter be treated as if she were blind and never be allowed to move around unaided; we must expect that paranoid hallucinations would increase as awareness of people and activities around her declined. This was the most productive and cordial meeting we'd had with Dr. Z at the hospital. I wish I could separate that impression from the fact that it began with me complimenting him several times in an effort to garner good will towards my poor old Dad.

During this conversation, I requested that Lonnie no longer be assigned as my mother's nurse, and made my reasons clear. I slept in the following morning and arrived at ten to find Lonnie once again on duty: this meant that Mom was still lying in bed, shouting at nobody, crabby, unkempt, and unfed. I sat down heavily in the chair beside her, the wind knocked out of me. Would she ever leave this place? Every conference with Dr. Z focused on stabilizing her condition, but what would stability look like? Did I want her completely passive and doped up? Would she be happier that way? To what lengths was I willing to go in order to "manage" her behavior and get my mother out of the hospital?

For better or for worse, I continued to protect my father from awareness of how poorly Mom was doing. When he visited and saw her functioning at what was currently her best, he was beside himself with distress, fussing and fretting, trying to refresh memories she had lost and practically force-feeding her as he lectured about vitamins and minerals. For my part, I had come to accept that her disinclination to eat made every bite that passed her lips a cause to celebrate: a couple of Cheerios, a piece of old Halloween candy, a leftover drumstick from my own lunch, a cold breakfast sausage. Daddy worked so hard at lunchtime to show Mom the benefits of healthy eating that he usually ended up consuming much of the tray himself. When he pressed half a sandwich into her hand she'd respond with a vague smile, saying, "Why don't you eat this? It's good for you."

Exhausted, strained, and absent too often, I was receiving some pressure from my college to request a family medical leave for the remainder of the semester, an option I had no desire to take: however much I wanted to care for my mother, I felt trapped and ineffective at the hospital; however badly I was functioning at work, each class or committee meeting helped me reconnect with a level of competence that was central to my self-image. My nerves were fraying and it was only a matter of time before they snapped. In an effort to foster better communication on a particularly bad night, I called the behavioral health unit to ask that our geriatric care consultant be included in all discussions. The conversation did not go well. After hanging up, I sent an email to the consultant, copied to my sister:

158

10:28 PM –

> *I called to ask that they include you in communications... staff very resistant. After two calls (and a long time on hold), I was put through to a unit social worker. I have talked with her three times tonight, and am very upset. My mother has been in the hospital now for over two weeks, and I do not think her needs are being met....*
>
> *Dr. Z's current prescription is for Mom to receive a 1.0 mg dose of Haldol at noon and at five P.M., with smaller doses of Haldol and Ativan to be administered if needed. The social worker says that tonight's record shows the following:*
>
> *Mom was given 0.25 mg each of Haldol and Ativan at ten A.M. today. (These are optional doses, with no cause recorded; when I showed up seventy-five minutes later the nurse did not disclose this to me).*
>
> *Mom was given 1.0 mg Haldol at 12:18 P.M. (I know that this is not true, because Dad and I were with Mom continuously from 11:45 until 1:30, and no meds were administered – when I asked the nurse whether Mom had already gotten the noon dose of Haldol before we came in, he said "yes").*
>
> *Mom was given 0.25mg Haldol + 0.25mg Ativan at 4:35because of combative behavior.*
>
> *Mom was given 1.0 mg Haldol at 5:57 P.M. (this is the dose that was supposed to be given at five, assuming that she had received her noon dose sometime close to noon – which I know for sure she did not)*

After recapping these concerns about medication, I wrote out my perception of sloppy record-keeping and nursing care. The email ended this way:

My goals: I want two things: I want my mother out of the hospital as soon as possible, and I want my mother's care to be as consistent as possible.

My apologies: I am sorry that I yelled at the hospital social worker tonight, and I must assume that she is doing her best. But I am at my wit's end. I do not think that the responses I was getting tonight on the phone (it's too complicated to have the staff talking with a consultant to the family... Dr. Z is out of town so there's nobody in charge...) are sufficient.

Before sending this email, I searched the hospital website for a way to copy it to Dr. Z. No luck.

That night, I also emailed my old friend Kathy:

Though the situation remains kind of impossible, your music suggestion is great! Maura loaded something like 150 songs into an iPod, set it into a simple dock, and sent it out here for Mom's use. She's had some nice moments with it... The cord was confiscated at the hospital, so we're running on batteries these days. A metaphor, perhaps, for my own weak power sources.

"Why don't you write that night the way it really happened?" my husband asks. That's precisely what I'm doing, I protest, but he is having none of it. "You were out of control," he says. "When you started shouting and swearing at that social worker, you were crying so hard I didn't know what to do."

Guilty as charged: I'm not telling the whole story. I don't remember exactly what profanity rose to my lips at the end of that "conversation," but I could easily make something up. Let's try, "How the hell can my mother improve if you people won't give her the fucking meds on time?" Or maybe, "I'm sick of this bullshit!" I was vaguely aware that my husband and daughter, sitting silently together in the kitchen, could hear my angry caterwauling and that it upset them, but by then I only cared about one thing: what the goddamn fucking hell would it take to get my mother out of that shitty hospital?

Anyway, there are many reasons not to write the scene with too much detail. Storytelling is a self-serving act, as the teller chooses what to emphasize and creates him- or herself as a character: doggedly devoted, tenderhearted, a little hapless, always sympathetic. Never mind that my anger was justified, it was ugly. I lost control. If the hospital social worker had been able to listen beyond her own defensive posture, she would perhaps have heard me for what I was that night: a desperate daughter, impotent in my frustration and fear, my tongue sufficiently loosened by alcohol to shout what I had been thinking night and day for two weeks but was too compliant and polite to say aloud.

So why don't I dwell on that scene, bring it to life in words? Because it makes me cringe. Sometimes I hate remembering.

Dr. Z phoned me around seven the following morning. He had obviously heard a full report from the social worker on duty the night before, and he made no attempt to conceal his aggravation. "What is it you want from me?" he barked, his voice rising. "One day you like us, the next day you act like we can't do anything right." I tried to sound conciliatory, but I had to make clear my concerns about the declining quality of nursing Mom was receiving, the inconsistent timing of ordered medication, the inaccurate record keeping... Dr. Z. cut me off. "I don't need to hear all that again," he snapped. I could not overlook his attitude for another moment. "Look," I told him, struggling against the impulse to start screaming again, "I can hear that you're feeling irritable about this, and I know that it's been difficult to work with Mom. Please understand that my father and I are exhausted. It's been even more difficult for us."

Dr. Z's tone moderated from anger to something more like weary annoyance. "OK. Here's what we'll do," he said. "Let's just get this over with so I don't have to deal with it anymore. We'll discharge her this morning and see what happens." *Let's just get this over with? So you don't have to deal with it anymore?* Does a doctor have the right to choose whether or not to help a patient in need? I began to ask whether it was safe to discharge Mom, but he cut me off again. "My staff will take care of everything. Give your mother until tomorrow before visiting her at Cascia Hall, and keep your father away through the weekend."

And just like that – after sixteen days of hospitalization – my mother was loaded into an ambulance and carted back to Cascia Hall.

A Riff on Words That Start with "H", Including *Hospital, Hype, Hippocrates,* and *Healing*

In a panel of Walt Kelly's *Pogo,* my favorite comic strip of all time, one of the denizens of the Okeefenokee swamp mentions that the doctor swore "a Hippocratical oath." Misheard by another critter, the poor doctor gets labeled "a hypocritical oaf." I relish a random memory of phoning my husband from the dramatic lounge on the acute care floor at Morana Hospital, the skyline of Milwaukee at my feet, and hearing him allude to this gag during our conversation. Sometimes, timing is everything.

The new Morana Hospital was inaugurated in October, 2010, after a multi-year building project that brought together two smaller, older community hospitals. My mother was admitted three weeks to the day after the doors officially opened. On the hospital's website, this new incarnation was announced in suitably glowing terms:

> *... we are committed to be leaders in the transformation of health care through our Call to Action to provide Health Care That Works, Health Care That Is Safe and Health Care That Leaves No One Behind. Our exciting new hospital will help us sustain and grow that mission for decades to come.*

Looking past the florid capitalizations and the creepy Bush-era echoes of a phrase like "Leaves No One Behind," there's no denying that the new hospital is an exciting structure, with its soaring atriums, tasteful lounges and dramatic views over the city and Lake Michigan. Opening any facility of this magnitude is bound to be very complex, so the confusing or missing signage we encountered when my mother was admitted shortly after is excusable... though I did, at one point, mistakenly open an

163

unmarked, unlocked door onto the burn unit, which definitely should have been off-limits to a casual passerby.

Among the hospital's many fine features, it occupies a prime piece of real estate conveniently situated next door to the retirement complex where my parents had come to dwell. For someone who could walk, the stroll from Umbria Court to Morana Hospital's main entrance would take just a few minutes; for someone with restricted mobility, like my father, the distance from the hospital's main entrance to the elevators and then to the desired unit upstairs can be prohibitively long and difficult, though he spent much of my Mom's two week hospitalization insisting that he would walk over from his apartment and back instead of waiting for me to pick him up.

In the months since my mother's death, I have wondered whether the newness of the "new" Morana Hospital may have played a role in the chaos of her care, but I keep coming up short. If my mother was "left behind" by a good deal of the hospital care she received, the problem was never the architecture or state-of-the-art facilities: it was communication. "Patient advocacy" was welcomed, in my experience, by most of the nursing staff, but doctors and social workers tended to treat my father and me as a nuisance, like little nipping flies that buzzed about their heads distracting them from more important business. While I own up to having had my moments of irritability, usually when I called at night to check on Mom and could not get information, I also had a great deal of guidance from the Cascia Hall social worker and the geriatric care consultant about what questions to ask, and how to communicate effectively with overworked hospital personnel. I took notes and tried not to waste anyone's time; the fact that my father, with his endless repetition and anxiety, did waste their time is beside the point: you don't have to be Jesus Christ to forgive an old man for acting scared and confused when his wife is *in extremis.*

One year after the new Morana Hospital campus opened, I checked the website to make sure that I was correct about something I vaguely remember being told by a hospital social worker: that Dr. Z, the geriatric psychiatrist, was the only geriatrician available on staff. A site search for "geriatrics" brought me to a page that defined the field and indicated, "There are presently no physicians with this specialty." Between the definition and that statement, two unfamiliar names appeared. Clicking on each of these names led to the impressive resumes of two geriatricians affiliated with the hospital, one of whom listed "dementia" among his "special interests," and the other of whom listed "memory disorders."

Refining my site search, I typed in "geriatric psychiatry." This again brought up a page that defined the field and said, "There are presently no physicians with this specialty." Between these two statements appeared the name of a specialist, in this case Dr. Z, and clicking on the name led me to his resume.

Intrigued, I started searching the site using other key words relevant to my mother's hospitalization: "There are presently no physicians with this specialty," the website informed me in response to a search for "inpatient psychiatric care" or "in-patient behavioral medicine," although my mother spent a week on a fully staffed in-patient psychiatric unit a year before. Searches for "Alzheimer's care" and "dementia care" deposited me at random points in the physician directory, the former including a pediatrician, an oral surgeon, and my own orthopedist. "Eldercare" didn't even get me that far.

Judging an institution by its slipshod website may seem superficial, but this lack of clear communication is symptomatic of my family's experience with Morana Hospital. And our experience reflects systemic flaws in healthcare delivery highlighted by Jack Resnick, a doctor who believes that elders are better served by treatment outside of the hospital environment. In an op-ed piece in the New York Times, he writes, "For too long the institutions that make up our health care system — hospitals, insurers and drug companies — have told us that 'more is better': more medicines, more specialists, more tests." His argument in favor of minimizing the hospitalization of elders is that home care "decreases the infections, mistakes and delirium, which, especially among the elderly, are the attendants of hospital care… To rein in spending and deliver better care," he concludes, "we must recognize that the primary mission of many an institution is its own survival and growth." In *A Bittersweet Season,* Jane Gross is more blunt in her advice for caregivers of elderly parents: "Stay out of emergency rooms and hospitals to the extent possible."

My sister and I have a lot of education and big vocabularies; even in the absence of the nursing home staff and a consultant to advise me, I would have begun a search for services by typing in "geriatrics" or "geriatric psychiatry," not "Alzheimer's." My sister and I have strong research skills and the confidence to speak up. If, thanks to poor communication, our mother was "left behind" in her care at Morana Hospital, what of the demented elder who comes to the ER after a bad fall and has no one to advocate for him/her? What of the family member who means to advocate for an elderly parent but lacks the education to frame needed questions?

If, to indulge a fantasy, Dr. Z and I were to meet over a cup of coffee for a heart-to-heart talk about my mother's treatment in her weeks at Morana Hospital, what would I say to him? The question is purely rhetorical, both because he does not strike me as the sort of man who spends a lot of time reflecting upon the quality of his relationships with his patients, and because I hope never to see him again. With the distance of time and the clarity of hindsight I'm still struggling to contextualize my anger and frustration. I am also trying to be fair: after all, he is a doctor who, for better or worse, has devoted his career to a patient population for whom the outlook is relentlessly depressing. To be a geriatric psychiatrist means to work with elders who face a foreshortened future impaired by loss, depression, anxiety, psychosis, and dementia. This cannot, by any measure, be an easy row to hoe.

I believe that Dr. Z meant to "treat" my mother's disease as best he could: using drugs and environmental adjustments, he meant to limit the troubling manifestations of her advanced dementia. Treating symptoms within a specialty is, after all, what modern doctors are trained to do. In an age in which many medical specialists complete their education prepared to focus on a single system or a single organ, even those whose organ of choice is the brain are ill equipped to see the patient as a whole person.

To become a doctor, Dr. Z must have recited the Hippocratic oath, which would have included some version of this language:"I do not treat a fever chart or a cancerous growth, but a sick human being, whose illness may affect the person's family... My responsibility includes these related problems, if I am to care adequately for the sick." And later, "I will remember that there is art to medicine as well as science, and that warmth, sympathy, and understanding may outweigh the surgeon's knife or the chemist's drug." The oath of Maimonides, which has sometimes been used as an alternative to the Hippocratic Oath, states, "May I never see in the patient anything but a fellow creature in pain."

Dr. Z did a fine job of counseling my family when my parents both lived at home, and when the questions we brought to him were relatively clear cut: twice we had consulted him about whether or not to go forward with surgeries recommended by other specialists, treatments which my sister and I believed to be riskier for an octogenarian patient with Alzheimer's than simply doing nothing at all. In both instances, my father felt bullied by the clergy of medicine and could not bring himself to say no. My sister and I were grateful that Dr. Z was able to reason with him and spare Mom unnecessary trauma.

When my mother fell down hard and landed in Morana Hospital with Dr. Z as her supervising physician, we learned by experience the limits of his practice. Though her physical injury was ugly, her hospitalization was, from the start, all about pharmacological behavior management. Dr. Z's contacts with her were brief, hurried, and impersonal: striding into her room, he'd ask, "How are you, Vivian?" then immediately step back out into the corridor to scrawl new orders for medication in her chart. My mother's emotional distress and my father's anxiety seemed almost beside the point. That big supra orbital bump notwithstanding, was there really a reason to keep her so long on the acute care ward? If the alien hospital environment was accelerating the deterioration of her cognitive function, why were we pushed to approve her move to the behavioral health unit? Would there have been any extended hospitalization at all if my parents did not have quality health insurance? Although Dr. Z repeated that he did not want to simply "drug her up and send her home," that appeared to be the best strategy contemporary medicine placed at his disposal.

When Dr. Z looked at my mother, what did he see? Was she just one more in an endless stream of old ladies whose brains are so mucked up by plaques and tangles that their behavior spins out of control? And what of my father and me? Were we just a couple more impossible family members who asked too many questions and expected miracles from him?

Diane Meier, Director of the Hertzberg Palliative Care Institute of Mt. Sinai Hospital and a MacArthur grant recipient, states, "There is a misperception on the part of the medical profession that patients and families only look to us for a technical cure. Patients and families look to us for partnership – for a healing relationship, for connection and commitment – not just as technicians." Dr. Z repeatedly reminded us that there was little that medicine can do for a patient with Alzheimer's, but he missed the point that there is quite a lot that *a doctor* can do to alleviate suffering. "Cure sometimes, treat often, comfort always," Hippocrates wrote. My parents' primary physician, Dr. Y, took the time to check on my mother every day, to hold her hand and listen to her, though he was not the attending physician at the hospital; he telephoned my father regularly, knowing full well that the conversation would be repetitive and my father would retain no information beyond the fact that he had cared enough to call. In all matters related to my mother's care, Dr. Y deferred to Dr. Z, and he seemed to have little idea what treatment might be helpful; even so, his engagement, his humanity, made both of my parents (and me) feel better.

I have no illusions that anyone in the world could have protected my mother from the delusions and terrors of late-stage Alzheimer's. However, she was blessed to be in contact with a number of people who took a truly Hippocratic approach to

168

eldercare: because they regarded Mom as "a fellow creature in pain," Kevin and Verna are good examples of the effectiveness of responding to a dementia patient in ways that communicate love and security, which in turn foster sufficient calm to enable that patient to accept companionship and basic care. In this, they joined the underpaid but sensitive staff at Cascia Hall, whose "warmth, sympathy, and understanding... outweigh the surgeon's knife or the chemist's drug."

Early in my mother's hospitalization, one of my older colleagues sent me a commiserating email in which he recalled a childhood visit to his grandmother who had been institutionalized for "senility." At that time and in that place, there was no such thing as a dedicated "memory care" facility with a well-trained staff. His gothic description of a dark, looming asylum filled with howling inmates tied to their beds seemed thankfully distant from my mother's environment.

Still, it isn't hard to see how dementia continues to become conflated with madness, for both imprison the sufferer in an altered reality. My mother was often crazy with fear at the end of her days, wild-eyed and raving even when I was holding her in my arms. In past times, her behavior may have been attributed to demonic possession or witchcraft. Again, it is Hippocrates who receives credit for overthrowing the belief that disease came from superstitious or divine origins. Disease, he argued, rose from natural sources, and the physician's efforts were better spent on accurately observing and alleviating symptoms than on speculating about supernatural causes of them. I can only wonder how an incomprehensible illness like Alzheimer's dementia appeared to his contemporaries. There were moments when my mother seemed, even to me, to be possessed, wrestling with demons that could never be exorcised.

One tragic irony of my mother's affliction with Alzheimer's is that throughout her career as a clinical psychologist her sole focus was alleviating the pain of fellow creatures. Her work embodied the healing power of "warmth, sympathy, and understanding." Perhaps hers would seem like very soft science to a doctor who came of age in a specialized, high tech environment, but her temperament and professional sensibility was finely tuned to Hippocrates' belief that each patient must be seen as a whole person, not just a collection of systems. Thus, she made it her business to reach out a healing hand to the most isolated and tortured souls, particularly those suffering in childhood.

Which brings me back to the fantasy of sitting down over a cup of coffee with Dr. Z to reflect on how each of us experienced the last days of Mom's life: above all, I would want him to learn who his patient – who my mother – truly was.

An Aside

A few days before Mom's discharge, the Cascia Hall social worker telephoned and asked me to stop by on my way home from Morana. Because she had been in touch with both Dr. Z and Dr. Y, and she had visited the hospital to assess Mom's condition for herself, I arrived at her office sweating with fear that she might refuse to take my mother back: what if this meeting was scheduled to tell me that Mom's paranoia and violence were too much for her staff? If the hospital nurses could not manage my mother's outbursts, if I felt incapable of caring for her twenty-four hours a day, how could I expect anyone else to do so?

I need not have worried. Holding both my hands in her own she told me, "We'll take care of your mother. That's not a problem. But she won't go easy: she is not going to have the peaceful death she deserves, and there is little any of us can do to make this better."

IV.

"She's gone. I've lost her, but I'm still responsible for her living, breathing body and the ghosts in her head."

-- Eleanor Cooney, *Death in Slow Motion*

Thanksgiving

My mother left the hospital on November eighteenth. Three days later, the twenty-first, was to be my parents' fifty-ninth anniversary. My parents customarily celebrated their marriage with their children, and they set the tone for dramatic commemorations. For their twentieth, they took my sister and me to Yucatan, an almost frighteningly adventurous trip in 1971: at the age of fourteen, I remember flying in a rickety six-seater plane over endless folds of jungle that sloped down to the Caribbean; the pilot pointed out an uninhabited stretch of coast that would someday become Cancun and said, "Someone wants to build a hotel down there." For their thirtieth a professional photographer shot portraits of the family. For their thirty-fifth, my sister and I prepared custom-made fortune cookies containing memorable quotes from our father. We spent a week in Palm Beach for their fortieth, enjoying a catered dinner complete with helium balloons that nearly traumatized their grandchildren, all under the age of four and unable to keep hold of the strings – what a chorus of wailing as those perfect red orbs drifted up, inevitably, into the tropical sky! In Tucson for their fiftieth, their four grandchildren wrote and performed a hilarious play based upon all the stories they'd heard of Mom and Dad's romance.

Coming up on Thanksgiving weekend 2010, we found ourselves in uncharted territory. I had expected to see my mother comfortably settled at Cascia Hall well in advance of the holiday; she would come to my house for Thanksgiving dinner, I imagined, and perhaps for an anniversary party the following day... at the very least, I thought, we would share a family dinner on the skilled nursing floor.

Once Mom fell, however, all bets were off. Perhaps she would spend Thanksgiving in the hospital? By the time Dr. Z lost his temper at me and dismissed her from his care, it was too late to reserve the nursing home's one private dining room. In any case, both the social worker and the geriatric care consultant discouraged us from having a family meal with ten people in attendance: they advised that we come to see Mom in ones or twos throughout the holiday weekend, being careful to downplay references to Thanksgiving, my parents' anniversary, or family traditions.

Not much happened on the actual day of my parents' fifty-ninth anniversary. Dad and I visited Mom for lunch and a few hours after. She was uninterested in food, had difficulty swallowing, yelled with frustration when an aide tried to wash her face, drifted in and out of awareness of who we were. I think my husband joined us for a while. We brought my father back to our house for the evening, while Verna came and sat with my mother.

Next morning, the Cascia Hall social worker drew me into her office for another confidential talk. "I thought that your mother had several months left," she told me, "but she lost a lot of ground in the hospital. I believe now that we are looking only at weeks." Though there was never any question where we were headed, though in my darkest moments I had even wished for my mother's misery to be over, that word weighed down my heart like an anchor: *weeks.* She explained the importance of hospice care and what support she could facilitate. I sat there reminding myself to breathe. Fifty-nine years of marriage. How could I tell this to my father?

Despite Dad's reluctance and my reliance on euphemisms, we met with representatives of a hospice agency the following day. The core hospice team – an administrator, a social worker, and a hearteningly passionate young nurse – explained what they could offer: safer and more comfortable furnishings, extra attention from specially trained aides, closer supervision by a nurse with the authority to administer palliative medications, emotional support for the family, and Medicare coverage for all of the above. As my father fidgeted in his chair, I read his every glance as an accusation of betrayal: was I giving up on my mother? Should I still be fighting to make her better?

At the end of the meeting, Dad dubiously agreed to hospice care. He seemed so wounded I could hardly meet his gaze. I reminded him about my friend whose mother-in-law had entered

176

and left hospice care half a dozen times in the past decade, knowing as I said it that this was not a desirable journey for a patient with advanced Alzheimer's. Within an hour or two, the young nurse had assessed my mother and written up new orders for palliative medication, and a hospice aide came to sit with her the following morning.

For decades, Thanksgiving preparations in my family have had a familiar rhythm. I would clean the house, make up beds for my sister's family, pack the refrigerator with groceries, and prepare pies, cranberry sauce, and squash casserole in advance. The day before Thanksgiving, my mother and I would pick up the turkey, bring it home and stow it somewhere that made us laugh – perhaps the garage, or the un-insulated front foyer of our house that my children dubbed "the chapel." There, the turkey slowly thawed while we worked on the most important element of the meal: the stuffing.

As a newlywed, I prided myself on making a rustic Thanksgiving dinner. I stuffed a goose with wild rice, wild mushrooms, pine nuts, and homegrown Brussels sprouts. But as my mother aged it became clear that she wanted the dinner prepared *her* way. I swallowed my pride, ordered a turkey, and asked Mom for her stuffing recipe ("2 bags of Pepperidge Farm sage and onion stuffing mix; 1 bag of Pepperidge Farm cornbread stuffing mix; 1 pint of liquid margarine; Bell's seasoning..."). Thereafter, on the last Wednesday of November, my mother and I spent a couple of hours dicing onions and celery, stirring chicken boullion cubes into packaged stuffing mix, adding salt and liquid margarine and whatever seasonings were included in that yellow box marked "Bell's." We kneaded the mixture with our hands, packed it into the biggest pot in the house, and found a cool place to leave it overnight, perhaps beside the turkey in "the chapel." This process took a measure of forbearance on both of our parts: my mother resented my improvisations, and I resented her tendency to over-instruct; did it really matter, when I was forty years old, whether or not I sliced celery exactly her way? I made a

177

point of rising extra early on Thanksgiving morning to stuff the oversized turkey, lace it up, and rub it with herbs before she woke and began to meddle.

On Thursday, November 25, 2010, my father and I shared "Thanksgiving Dinner" with Mom at noon. Everything on the table at Cascia Hall – turkey, stuffing, cranberry sauce, creamed green beans, and pumpkin pie – had the consistency of lumpy mashed potatoes. My mother followed my lead into brief reminiscences about her parents, but refused to eat. When I fed her, she spit the food out and coughed. I felt heartsick leaving her to go home and roast a turkey for her grandchildren, and I can only imagine how my father felt. When my sister and her husband arrived later in the afternoon, we sat down to a meal that seemed anything but festive.

The anniversary custom proved particularly problematic: with my mother in hospice care and unable to leave the nursing home, what was the appropriate way to celebrate the unlikely *mitzvah* of our parents' love? My sister and I dialed back ten years and reproduced the poem Mom had written to honor their 49th anniversary. Once again, our mother saved the day.

November, 2000
THE FORTY-NINERS
by Vivian Harway

Louise's husband, Al, offered to take the pictures.
Only a few came out, most of those were blurred
Or heads were cut off.

We do not need them. They are stored in the gallery of
     our minds.
Photos fade, get lost, we wonder who these faces are.
Memories endure, and show us more.

My parents, fogbound in Newark on their first trip by air,
Arriving breathless, as the judge made his entrance.
Sheer force of maternal will raised the airport clouds.

Your mother, escorted by dear Uncle Charlie,
Anticipating some unknown calamity, but bravely smiling.
Sharing, with my mother, the unspoken certainty
That from this day forward, each of their children
Was lost to them forever.
Time and love would prove them wrong.

A tipsy judge, the sole jurist willing to come out on
     this holiday eve,
Stumbled over some lines that we, repeating after him,
     made solemn.
To have, to hold, to cherish, to love, as long as we
     both shall live.

We faced the future with confidence and joy.
Our friends, gathered to rejoice and celebrate with us,
Made our simple ceremony merry and memorable.

Forty-nine years have passed since that happy, anxious day.

179

Nine and forty years attest to our constant love.
Seven times seven years, as the sage might intone.

Good times, bumpy times, more smooth than rough times,
Good health, good children, good grandchildren, good friends,
One good dog, and two bossy iguanas,
And, dayenu, our parents were happy.

Here we stand: Forty-niners who have traveled long
    and far together,
And found treasure on the journey to rival Sutter's gold.

Growing Small Again

When my sister was little, her favorite toy was a big red fire engine. It rolled smoothly around the rocking chair where my mother cuddled me in a fluffy pink blanket while I drank my bottle, and across the carpet underneath the changing table where my mother seemed always to be busy with me. The fire engine had a little silver handle you turned to extend the ladder, little rubber hoses to pull out and put back, little doors to open and shut. This was long before the word "feminism" became common in popular usage, but it's no accident that my mother's oldest daughter was set to enter pre-school with an androgynous collection of toys.

My mother loved to tell of my sister's belief that growing up was a two-way street: children grew bigger and bigger until they became grown-ups, and eventually grown-ups grew smaller and smaller until they were children again. In this way, as she played alone, jealous of my mother's attentions to me, she could look forward to a time when Mom would have nothing in the world to do but play with her.

Between bottles and diapers one day, my mother received a phone call and spent most of an hour in rapt conversation with an old friend. My sister kept herself busy with her toys until Mom hung up, then asked, "Who was that?" Mom said it was her friend Pete. "Is he nice?" Yes, my mother assured her, he was a very nice person. My sister considered, then said, "When he grows small again, I will let him play with my fire engine."

My mother was not a small person. She was a leggy, striking woman who stood up straight, and the combination of high heels and the way she wore her hair through the sixties and seventies – in an intricate bun coiled on top of her head – added to her stature. When she entered a room, people noticed. In midlife she grew heavy and in old age she grew stooped, but her bearing was impossible to overlook.

This strong presence is one of the first things Alzheimer's stole from her. Increasingly befuddled by her surroundings, Mom grew passive in situations she could not follow. Sometimes she kept up a brave front, laughing when everyone else laughed, murmuring generic conversational staples like, "My, my," or "Isn't that something." Later on, she simply withdrew from the perplexing chatter around her, closing her eyes, both present and absent at once.

Prior to her fall, I had frequently helped Mom to bathe or dress. I was aware that she'd lost quite a bit of weight, but it seemed like no cause for alarm. Suddenly, strangely, I found myself coaxing her to eat tiny meals, recreating the ways my husband and I had made food seem more fun to our finicky preschoolers twenty years earlier: would she eat if her sandwich looked like a smiley face? Would she like fingers of toast to dip into applesauce or yogurt? My father, unable to part with his wife's adult intelligence, lectured about nutrition. I had more success with Mom at mealtimes, but that's not saying much.

In *Remembering the Music, Forgetting the Words*, a heartfelt memoir about nursing her mother through dementia, Kate Whouley writes that, "An Alzheimer's patient follows the reverse path of learning and remembering. First, we forget the most recent things we've learned – what we had for lunch, perhaps – and then we forget how to make lunch. Next we forget we need to eat lunch. Ultimately, we will forget how to eat lunch. In the end, we will forget the first things we learned in this life: how to suck and how to swallow." When my mother entered the hospital she had more or less forgotten the need to eat lunch. Two weeks later, she returned to Cascia Hall many pounds lighter and dangerously close to the last steps of forgetting.

With the benefit of hindsight, it's clear that I chose not to see how fast she was diminishing. In acute care, she wanted the room kept dark and never wore more than a hospital gown or a bathrobe. Then, on the behavioral health unit there was a distinct shift in her posture: seated in the ugly vinyl recliner, she'd draw her knees to her chest and rest her chin upon them. Her legs looked flexible and girlish that way, though they could support her less and less. The comfortable clothes I was encouraged to bring from home hung from her shoulders, revealing a birdlike neck and the prominent clavicle that looked so dramatic in pictures from when she was young.

Around the time Mom returned to Cascia Hall, she stopped walking altogether. Functionally blind and unable to recover whatever muscle tone she'd had before the fall, she hardly seemed to notice the transition from walker to wheelchair. Once in a while I'd come in to find her curled like a kitten on the loveseat in her room, drifting somewhere between sleep and waking, and I'd wonder if I could move her feet gently enough to squeeze in beside her, to rest with her. I was the big person now: it was my job to spoon food to her lips, to make sure her bottom was clean. I wanted more than anything to hold her in my lap and rock her.

The week before my mother died, I brought my younger dog, Curtis, to visit her. She was slipping farther and farther away from conversation or even singing; I thought that spending time together stroking velvety basset-hound ears might be therapeutic for us both.

Curtis made a grand entrance coming off the elevator. His stubby-legs, taciturn demeanor, and tuxedo markings give him the appearance of a miniature Edwardian butler, and everyone in the dayroom wanted to pet him. His only faux pas was pulling rather too hard toward the kitchen.

At last we made our way down the hall to my mother's room. She was lying in bed, covers pulled up to her chest. Her body appeared impossibly small, an undefined and flattened form barely lifting the blankets. She whispered to herself as her hands gestured vaguely, thin and aimless as bare branches stirred by breeze.

"Look who came to see you, Mom," I said. Eyes closed, she mumbled, "Who's there?" "Look, Mom," I said again, "It's my dog Curtis." She smiled, repeated his name, but didn't open her eyes. "Here," I said, pushing Curtis close to the bed, "he loves it when you pet his ears. Feel how soft they are." Her right hand reached vaguely out and up, a good three feet over the dog's head, and I guided it down to rest. Though Mom smiled for a moment, there was no sign that she knew what was going on. There was

183

none of the free association back to dogs of her childhood that I had dreamed of wakening again. She moved her hand slowly back and forth a couple of times on Curtis's head, then lifted it to her chest and turned away. The hair at her neck stuck to her skin in sweaty curls, like a baby's after a nap. I could tell from her breathing that she'd gone back to sleep.

In Kate Whouley's words, "No one dies of Alzheimer's. The disease does not ravage the body the way a terminal cancer does. Alzheimer's patients simply forget how to stay alive." For so long I had bemoaned the fact that I was losing my mother to Alzheimer's, but in the end, it was she who lost connection to the world and drifted away like a balloon from the fist of a child who means to hold fast to that precious string forever.

"Readjustment"

The Cascia Hall staff was remarkably effective at getting my mother up, bathed, and dressed every morning. In a caregiving tournament, they would have left the nurses and aides from Morana Hospital choking on their dust. What made their performance so extraordinary, however, was their ability to foster cooperation on the part of oppositional patients. Like my poor, terrified mother.

There was a sense of settling down that accompanied Mom's return from the hospital. It was not, by any measure, a rosy period: there were simply a few more welcome moments of calm between my mother's storms of screaming and tearing off her clothes. The voices that ordered her to undress threatened to torture her if she resisted. She sobbed, cowering and clawing at herself to rip the fabric away from her skin. Paradoxically, this particular delusion tended to strike early in the day; after gently coaxing her to dress again, sometimes two or three times per morning, the staff could pretty much count on her remaining clothed until bedtime.

My father seldom visited before noon, and I saw no reason to describe these episodes to him. He kept me hopping, in any case, with his insistence that I hire someone to sit with Mom for every waking moment. I was back at work, and the Cascia Hall social worker challenged me: weren't her people enough? Not for my father. Each day I spent hours on the telephone, negotiating with the home-care agency: Verna was happy to come in every evening, but earlier shifts were up for grabs. I ended up booking caregivers I had not met, some of whom rubbed the nursing home staff the wrong way.

And each day I sat with my mother as well. Even if just for an hour or so, I held her hand, sang to her, tried to persuade her to open her eyes and look at photographs. I went to crazy lengths to make her sip an energy shake or thickened water as swallowing became burdensome for her. I sometimes felt jealous of the aides who could guide her to the toilet, coax her to eat a bite of pudding, encourage her to engage with the world for just a moment: if I

185

could hardly help her to drink or urinate, how could I remind her of the fifty years we'd shared as mother and daughter?

The first Friday in December, my cell phone rang before eight A.M. I was driving too fast on the freeway, running late to lead an all-day writing workshop and teacher in-service for a suburban school district. The caller was a case manager for the eldercare agency. When the aide I had hired for Mom arrived at Cascia Hall a half hour earlier, she reported, the room was a shambles, everything thrown around "like a tornado hit." My mother was sitting naked on the loveseat and sobbing. Alarmed, the aide called in to report that Mom was not receiving proper care.

I knew from experience how difficult it was to redirect my mother from the throes of a delusion. The caregiver's account, however, worried me. How could this degree of chaos go unnoticed? I left a message for the social worker to call me back the minute she arrived at Cascia. Hall, then dialed the nursing station to check on Mom's condition. No one picked up. Sick with anxiety, I started my day – five hours of programming for fifty fourth-graders plus a handful of teachers, and I was in charge of everything.

On the way home, I stopped at Cascia Hall to meet with the social worker and the head of nursing. They reminded me of the increasing challenge they faced to keep my mother calm enough to remain clothed in the morning. They explained that on this particular day, after getting Mom up, the aides had moved on to assist other residents and no one heard the hubbub as she stripped and hurled her clothes around the room. Calm down, they told me: the woman from the agency simply panicked. Instead of calling for assistance or helping Mom herself, she phoned her supervisor as if blowing the whistle on a case of extreme negligence.

I saw their point. The agency caregiver meant well: if you haven't spent much time with an Alzheimer's patient, how would you judge this chaos "normal?" I understood my father's need to have a proxy sitting beside Mom for every waking moment. And I couldn't fault the social worker for adamantly requesting that we cut back on all the outside care and place our trust in her staff. We had hospice aides who worked in harmony with the nursing home staff, and Verna had won everyone's respect: could we please just stop hiring these morning people?

For a few moments, I sat silently before these two fine women who do the most difficult work in the world, and do it with love and respect for those in their care. They were right, of course, but I struggled to say so. Exhaustion buffeted me like a stiff wind; I leaned into it, barely able to hold myself upright.

Prayer

Though they raised us with a sense of Jewish identity, my parents preferred to keep their children at a decided distance from anything like organized religion. It's one of the finest features of my upbringing: we had room to explore, and it was never an effort to respect other belief systems so long as nobody forced anything upon their neighbors. Our family's atheism frequently got my sister and me into trouble on the playground, but that generally served to affirm our determination not to be like the kids who threw stones at us. Besides, it was easy to see that some of the taunting rose from jealousy: in the largely Catholic neighborhood where we spent our earliest years, nobody could frighten my sister and me with a lecture about sin or the torments of hell. It was as if we had marked a box labeled "N/A": we didn't study catechism or go to church, yet we excelled in school and were known as the best-behaved kids on the block.

I once asked my mother how much of Catholic doctrine she really believed when she was growing up. "All of it," she answered, "What else could I do?" She went on to explain that, naturally, she had doubts during adolescence, but Catholicism was a fundamental part of belonging to her family, her school, her church, her neighborhood, even her sorority in college. It wasn't until she left home for graduate school, where she became immersed in a diverse and progressive community and fell in love with my father, that she considered the possibility of following her questions into a different way of living.

I replay that conversation in my mind as I think about my mother's last days. If she believed unquestioningly in a Catholic version of the afterlife as a child, did that belief recur as the distant past became her lived reality? Shortly after her return to Cascia Hall, I entered her room one afternoon to find her lying in bed mumbling to herself, her right hand moving vaguely up and down, side to side, over her chest. "What are you doing, Mom?" I asked. Eyes closed, she remained indifferent to my presence. I dropped to my knees, leaning in as close as I dared to make out her slurred speech: "Forgive me for I have sinned."

Of course, at the time I didn't know, I couldn't know, that she would be dead within a week. Outside in the real world, Hanukkah was to begin at sundown; I already had a menorah set out in the dining room window. When Mom stirred from her reverie, I pretended I had just arrived, greeting her and giving her a kiss. I'm pretty sure she had no idea who I was, but she liked it that I called her beautiful and said "I love you." Beyond closed blinds the early darkness of a Wisconsin December evening was gathering. After a little while, I went home to light the candles with my children.

When I visited the next morning, Mom was sitting in the red Broda chair brought in by the hospice nurse. Designed to be more comfortable than a wheelchair, the Broda reduced the need for restraints by ergonomically discouraging whoever sat in it from rising. Her head was bowed and, once again, her right hand moved in graceful sweeps before her. "Are you praying, Mom?" I asked. She shook her head slowly: "No. No, no. Not praying."

For a moment I was able to hold her attention through touch, which increasingly supplanted language at the end. I rubbed lotion into her hands and commented on how much my own long, thin fingers look like hers; I brushed her hair and hummed to her. A few minutes later, her right hand rose again and shaped the cross before her chest. Then, bowing her head, she pressed her palms together and drew her hands to her lips. With that gesture – that deep memory of a gesture – I understood that no matter how much I wanted to keep her with me, my mother was going home.

Unfinished Business

Waking or sleeping, conscious or not, my mother has been with me for every moment of my life. She has held my hand, she has twisted my arm. She has hugged me close; she has choked the breath out of me. She is my pole star, and she is a comet slashing through what I thought I knew of space before disappearing.

Shortly after Mom's death, I dream that I must return to the funeral home to settle some unfinished business. My husband and I dress up like church-going folk on Sunday. We bring along our two grown children, my father, my sister, and a couple of friends for support. The funeral parlor resembles a design studio in the days before computers: great vast drafting tables with projects spread out, a creative-looking mess. The funeral director, even smarmier and more simpering than in real life, wants us to approve signage that will announce my mother's death to the world. He unveils the posters, which abstract a few photos of Mom into weird purple line drawings, captioned with florid words of praise in matching script (purple prose, quite literally). My father hates every bit of it, but is too polite to say so. I am not. "This was just a mistake," the funeral director fusses, "I'll correct it in no time at all."

Suddenly I notice a body, or a bundle that I take to be a body, lying on a drafting table nearby. It is wrapped in pastel printed fabric, little checks and flowers that put me in mind of calico curtains that luffed in the kitchen windows of the house where we lived for the first ten years of my life. I jump to conclusions, terrified that somehow the staff has forgotten propriety and kept my mother lying around like a pile of laundry.

No, the funeral director reassures us, this is someone else; it's just an innocent oversight, not to worry. I don't believe him for a minute. I wake in tears, wondering, what do I know of where my mother is now?

I'm not talking about her body. Flesh can last only so long, and we have a box of ashes we trust are hers, for whatever that's worth. I mean, where is my mother?

Religious notions of the afterlife generally leave me cold. Even if you dispense with judgmental constructs of Heaven and Hell, it's hard to imagine anything more depressing than all the souls from time immemorial crowding around in eternal idleness (when I hear talk of the rapture, it gives me the claustrophobic creeps). I do, however, believe in something that I think of as "spirit," an essence that animates life. Spirits watch and bless us when we move through the world as we're meant to, respectfully and appreciatively, when we do good simply because it is the right thing to do. Spirits, to me, manifest as the sense that a loved one is watching… or as a glistening black snake crossing my path like an omen of transformation.

In any case, dementia has a disturbing way of seeming to separate body and soul before death. Caterina Edwards, author of *Finding Rosa,* writes that "those suffering from Alzheimer's often wander. They do not 'get lost.' They are lost, permanently. And since everything around them is unrecognizable, they search for a place of certainty and familiarity that they (and we) call home." Mom started telling me she wanted to go home well before she was moved to Cascia Hall. Once, when I knocked on the door of my parents' apartment, she couldn't find a way to let me in. I stood out in the hallway, hearing her stomp around cursing "this place" as if she hadn't lived there for years. Our useless circular conversations sounded increasingly desperate, and the more difficulty she had placing one foot ahead of the other, the more likely she was to march out the back door of my house without her walker, insisting that she was "going home." By her last days, great blocks of her life had evaporated, including the half century in which being my mother was a central feature of her identity. At the end she recognized me as no more than a pleasant woman who dropped in from time to time, indistinguishable from any other caregiver.

In *Remembering the Music, Forgetting the Words*, Kate Whouley reflects on whether dementia might be a form of "soul wandering." The soul, preparing to depart, "begins leaving the body for short intervals, and these absences lead to the confusion of the mind and lack of orientation in the body that typify

Alzheimer's." This is not such a far-fetched notion. Jewish liturgy includes the *Modeh Ani,* a morning prayer that gives thanks for the soul returning to the body after traveling in dreams:

> *I thank you*
> *Living and enduring King*
> *Since you have restored my soul to me in compassion.*

I know the scientific explanations of the disease, of course, but I find this line of thinking particularly comforting. If both dementia and dreaming are forms of "soul wandering," perhaps there exists an ineffable dimension in which my mother and I can still find one another.

Last Words

Sometimes my mother sits in the recliner and sometimes on the loveseat. Once the Broda chair arrives, the staff tends to settle her there because it is adjustable and easy to wheel in and out at mealtimes. When she stops taking meals altogether, they send someone down to her room to coax a sip of thickened water between her lips, clear gelatinous glop that reminds me of Vaseline, or to help her eat a spoonful of chocolate pudding.

Sometimes my mother is in a pleasant mood and sometimes she shouts and cries. Once we accept the need for hospice care, she becomes indifferent to family visits. "She's starting to seem really out of it," my father tells me, day after day. I bring in my daughter and my dog. I show her photos of her parents and play music from her youth. If she makes the effort to speak at all, she slurs and drools, then turns away from me and dozes off.

Sometimes I brush her hair and sometimes I just hold her hand. Once I face the fact that she doesn't know or care who I am, we connect (insofar as we connect at all) through touch. Rubbing lotion into the pale, crinkly skin of her hands, I remember how, as a child, I loved tracing the maps of her pronounced veins outwards from the wrist, blue streams coursing to her long, immaculate fingers. She would ease her gold wedding band over the muscular knuckle and slip it onto my chubby finger. She would hold her hand up to my hand, palm to palm, so her fingers appeared impossibly long and graceful, towering over mine; then, grasping my hand with a loving squeeze and a shake, she'd promise that I would grow up to be beautiful and strong, before placing her wedding ring back on the finger it was meant for, the one with a vein running straight to her heart. In these last days, because she is growing so thin, her skin papery and almost translucent, her wedding ring slips off and tangles in the bed sheets. The nurse on duty finds it and returns it to my father. It lies in her jewelry box after that, the quaint little Bombay chest Dad gave her decades ago, which for so long my sister and I loved to open, to try on her treasures. The chest sits where it has always sat, on top of her yellow-wood dresser, identical to my father's dresser, the two of them side by side since the day they were purchased for the first bedroom my parents ever shared.

Holding my mother's fragile hand in my own, I wonder how we take the measure of a life. I'd like to say I have become her, but I haven't. She was a pioneer who pushed beyond the social and intellectual expectations of her upbringing; having been weaned on her vision of accomplishment, the best I can say is that I'm smart enough and I make a decent living. I'd love to claim that I blaze new trails, but I dawdle, safely defining myself as an under-achiever. I'd love to claim her long, graceful fingers as my own, look for the map of veins transposed beneath my skin, but my hands never were like hers. Mine are calloused and ruddy, the knuckles swell. I never outgrew the habit of biting my nails. Sometimes, near the end, Mom tolerates my petting. Sometimes she brushes me off and turns away.

On the weekend, I come in to find an unfamiliar hospice aide giving my mother a sponge bath. The radio is tuned to a station playing contemporary Christmas music, the kind of kitsch Mom hated, but as the young aide raises her arm to wash beneath it, her head lolls dreamily back against the wing of the chair.

In spite of myself, I feel jealous: I want my mother's attention, I want her to recognize *me*. I butt in with a big hug and a kiss, telling the aide, "I see that you've met my beautiful mother." The aide smiles, unfazed, but Mom seizes on the word: "Mother?" she cries, "*Whose* mother? Whose daughter are you?" "I'm your daughter, Mom." My voice sounds small and pathetic. But even at this late date Mom maintains a sense of propriety. "Of course you are," she replies, though I might as well be anyone.

As we chat, the aide mentions that she is working on a Masters degree in social work. I tell her that my mother, who at that moment is limp as the washcloth with which she is being bathed, was a clinical psychologist whose career involved working with disabled and abused children. Mom's eyes remain closed, her jaw slack, as I go on at more length than this young woman needs to

194

hear about her brilliance and distinction. "Her mentor was one of the earliest women to earn a PhD in child psychology," I state, "In fact I think she was the *second*."

With a start, Mom sits up straighter. "*Who* are you talking about?" she demands. "Frances," I say, "Wasn't she the second woman in child psychology?"

Mom shakes her head wildly from side to side. She looks like some great trapped animal straining at ropes, unable to rise from that chair. "You don't know what you're talking about," she rails, her voice aggrieved. "You don't even know what that word means."

The young aide and I exchange glances. "What word?" By now my mother is slurring back into incoherence, but we both understand her to say that the offending word "means easy to get a baby in your belly." And slowly, I begin to hear what my mother thinks she heard when I said "second." Her mentor had been a pioneer in the field, had raised a daughter while building an academic career, not a common blend of accomplishments for a woman born in 1893; resisting the pressure to choose between professional fulfillment and motherhood was also a cornerstone of Mom's adult life. No longer able to recognize the daughters for whom she herself had been a powerful role model, or her grandchildren who never questioned that their lives could balance family and meaningful work, Mom misheard and thinks I'm mocking her: that of all words I could use to describe her beloved early mentor, I had chosen "*fecund.*"

The Way I Want to Remember

I don't know what possessed me to photograph my mother in the hospital, but one day, sitting by her bedside on the acute care unit, I snapped a few pictures of her. She was lying on her back, dozing fitfully, and a shaft of light from the corridor fell through the half-opened door, illuminating the right side of her face. Perhaps I wanted to show my sister the severity of her injuries, or perhaps I wanted to prove to myself the reality of this seemingly surreal time and place. Or perhaps I was just looking for something to pass the time between crises.

All I had with me was my cell phone, a little flip phone with a shabby camera function I had used only once or twice before. Mom stirred slightly at each click of the shutter, then sighed back into unconsciousness as I stepped out into the hall to study captured images of the battered face I'd been gazing at day and night since her fall. I was startled by their clarity.

This was not my mother's face. Both gaunt and swollen at once, it appeared top heavy, with irregular bands of color crossing it like an evening sky. It was an encyclopedia of the color red: soft pink and burgundy, carmine and brick, peach, blowzy coral, and, inevitably, the plain flat sheen of drying blood. Close in to the eyes, the reds blended into browns and purplish blacks. The upper half appeared puffy and smooth, while the lower, paler half was creped in fine webs of wrinkles around the half-opened mouth, the sagging jaw line, the stalk of the neck. It was a horror of a face. I never wanted to forget it.

After moving her to the behavioral health unit, I photographed my mother once again. The light was better, in part because she consistently kept her eyes closed by this time and her calls to draw the curtains had ceased. She was sitting in one of those awful hospital recliners, hands in her lap, head angled slightly to the left. Except for some dark spots and the yellowing remnants of bruises, the coloring of her skin looked almost normal. The nose still was slightly swollen, the lips drawn down. In these pictures, the face is recognizable as my mother's, in the way that a wax museum figure is recognizable: features have familiar form and proportions, but there is a flatness of aspect such that you would not mistake this for a real person.

In one of our daily phone calls, I told my sister about the pictures. "That's a bad idea," she said. "You should delete them. Our job is to remember Mom the way she was before all this." She went on to tell me about a young colleague of hers who had died of cancer shortly before his daughter's Bat Mitzvah. At the Bat Mitzvah, his daughter had hung up a large photograph of him from a happy time in the family's life, and had given a small print to each guest. My sister kept it framed in her office and was looking at it as we spoke. "This is the way I want to remember him."

I see her point, of course. But Mom was not simply the dazzling young woman sitting cross-legged in the grass on the day my favorite picture of her was taken in 1952. She wore many faces in her eighty-five years and most, but not all, were beautiful. If I could write the script, I would spare her those last dreadful months of her life; I would give her a tranquil ending to her story. I never gave up on trying to comfort her, but there was precious little I could do beyond being a witness.

The morning Mom died, I spent a few hours alone in her room at Cascia Hall. I say "alone," though her body was there with me. I did what any daughter would do, kneeling beside her bed and sobbing into her chest. I begged her not to leave me. I sat and stared at her. Her face was pale, her lips parted, and if not for the fact that her skin was rapidly growing colder to the touch she might have been dreaming. When the nurse had called to inform me of her passing, she said Mom drew her last breath sometime between five-fifteen and five-thirty A.M.

In those quiet hours, before eight o'clock when I would call my father knowing that he was already up, before the hospice nurse was slated to arrive and fill out the death certificate, I photographed my mother one last time. I later lost all of these images because I never downloaded them and my phone gave up

197

the ghost. But I can see each clearly in memory, especially that last one, which I turn over and over in my mind like a wave-smoothed stone: I cannot document this, but I believe my mother died peacefully in her sleep.

V.

"My duty to care for her was done, but not my responsibility. I still struggled to understand the story of her life, to recover a few of her lost memories, to braid that rope bridge of stories over a sinkhole of oblivion."

-- Caterina Edwards, *Finding Rosa*

Memento Mori

I was raised to be too skeptical to believe in ghosts, but still the dead haunt me. My mother whispers from the folds of her old polyester blouses that I wear like tunics. She nudges my ribs, an unsettling sensation that eerily registers along the same spectrum as feeling a baby kick inside the womb when I drive past Morana Hospital, which is where, in many senses, she lost her life though she did not die until two weeks after discharge. She prowls the corridors of my sleep, trying every door, and wrings tears from my heart at unexpected moments. I cling to what she wore, to what she made, to what she left me, as if the things themselves embody memory.

"You should have this to remember her," my sister says, handing me a bulky parcel wrapped in tissue paper. "I think Mom would want you to have it."

It's late on a December evening, shortly after our mother's death. We are sitting in my living room drinking wine with our childhood friend Kathy, daughter of my mother's best friend. I chalk up the fact that I'm habitually drinking more than I should be to the stresses of caregiving, and I'm approaching the too-familiar buzz that both numbs me and keeps me from feeling completely numb these days. As I tear open the wrapping, my sister asks, "Remember when Mom took up rug-hooking?"

She's got me there. I remember our mother's embroidery, crocheting, knitting, sewing. I remember her drawing, making puppets, creating Halloween costumes and throwing the best birthday parties our neighborhood had ever seen. I remember her gardening, canning, and baking. But *rug-hooking*?

The paper falls away. The throw pillow in my hands is about eighteen inches square. On the hooked side, the background is bushy cream yarn with deep pile, and the design is an orange and brown sunburst that looks vaguely regal. There's a circle at the center, and sort of a *fleur de lis* form worked in around the outer

201

ring. The other side is plain white cotton, perhaps cut from an old pillowcase.

My sister gazes at me expectantly, mistaking my blank expression for a poor memory. "Don't you remember? She didn't do it for long because it was so tedious. This was supposed to be a whole rug," she laughs, "but Mom ran out of steam and turned it into a pillow. I'm pretty sure she drew the design herself."

I turn the pillow over a few times, feeling too tired to speak. Besides the fact that it is plug ugly, I vividly remember making this thing with my own hands. It was a kit someone had given me, probably in high school, and yes, the process of rug hooking was so tedious that it took an effort of will and several long evenings of TV watching to finish just this small square. Mom may have sewn the backing for me, I don't remember.

Not long ago I took my son to Goodwill to buy kitchenware for his new apartment. When he wandered off to try on a couple of shirts, I began leafing through racks of textiles: towels, placemats, curtains, random remnants of cloth clipped to coat hangers. Growing up, I paid little attention to my mother's attempts to educate us in the domestic arts. My sister learned to knit and crochet, to use a sewing machine, to iron properly, skills I never mastered. And yet, because I am drawn to textures and colors, to nubby, rough-spun yarns, to shimmers of gilt, to speckly tweeds, my hands and eyes immediately found pleasure in the selection of fabrics they clicked through in the Goodwill store.

Halfway down the rack, I found six hangers bearing identical crocheted placemats, each one an elongated hexagon of synthetic green, white, and purple yarn, unappealing and sloppily constructed. Their very awkwardness made me feel as though I was holding the hand of whoever made them. She – for she surely was a woman – would have been middle-aged, perhaps trying to develop new interests or hobbies as her children left home, a woman with creative impulses but little aesthetic sophistication. I could see her sitting before the television on a dark plaid couch, crocheting her way through the ten o'clock news and maybe

Johnny Carson, as her husband dozed nearby in his recliner. At Christmas, her family members would receive another set of placemats, another winter scarf, a throw pillow, an afghan. Whether or not they liked the colors, the family would smile and praise her craft; after that it's anyone's guess which articles got used and which spent years in a drawer somewhere before a day of spring cleaning sent them to Goodwill.

Those placemats undid me. Tears sprang to my eyes as I fingered their erratic loops and whorls, their concentric circles of colors that no one in their right mind would juxtapose. In their imperfection, I saw a crooked reflection of the far more skillful workmanship of my mother's afghans, which she began producing in almost alarming numbers while my sister and I were in college. At first she followed patterns to the letter, but eventually she started developing her own, with results that can only be described as mixed. Along with many beautiful creations, I still have a particularly hideous double spread pieced together of enormous black and white rectangles meant to look like dominoes; another, intended for her mother-in-law, is a jarring mash-up of browns and yellows, clearly an effort to use up remnants of yarn with no regard for appearance.

My mother's artistry grew through many evenings of sitting before the television on a dark plaid couch, crocheting her way through the ten o'clock news and maybe Johnny Carson, as her husband dozed nearby in his recliner, until each of her grandchildren, when they *finally* arrived, was swaddled in one-of-a-kind baby blankets designed with just that child in mind. The fine, soft infant yarn of the first blanket was replaced by bolder colors and more interesting textures in the second. As each child graduated from crib to bed, he or she received a full-sized afghan.

When my son was ready for his first full-sized afghan, Mom wrote a story to accompany the gift. Because she had raised only daughters and he was her only male grandchild, she never quite knew what to make of him; this storybook was possibly an attempt to mitigate the domesticity of the gift, to make it more masculine and appealing to a little boy. Stapled inside a manila folder and illustrated with awkward line drawings, it told of a native child named, with a disarming lack of political correctness, "Little Indian." When given his first blanket, Little Indian rides his pony out on the prairie to camp under the stars, wrapped in the colors of the sunset. My son loved the afghan, with its wavy horizontal lines of cream, mauve, and dark blue; not enough happened in the story to hold his attention.

I was tempted to buy those ugly placemats from Goodwill, but at this time of my life divesting makes much more sense than accumulating stuff, and it seemed unfair to inflict them on my son. He moves lightly through life, and prefers to avoid sentimental attachments to objects. Even his "Little Indian" blanket has been left behind to take its place as one of many afghans filling our closets. He can have it back any time he wants, but I will never get rid of it. Mom stopped crocheting when her eyesight began to fail, back when time still made sense to her; Alzheimer's caused her to forget that fact. "I haven't been crocheting much lately," she would comment every time someone complimented her handiwork, extending the meaning of "lately" to include more than a decade. It was something she was just about to get back to, right up to the end.

When we moved Mom into Cascia Hall, everyone advised us to decorate her room with familiar things that would make her feel at home. I framed dozens of pictures of family members, hauled over photo albums, hung two huge, framed embroideries she designed and stitched when I was a child, placed some of her jewelry in a box and some of her china tea-cups in a chest in the corner. And, of course, I brought in afghans. There was a cream-colored throw with matching pillows on the loveseat, a heavier granny pattern for winter in the closet; also, because it's light-weight and no one was using it, "Little Indian's" first blanket.

This last was a favorite of the nursing home staff. When they straightened up my mother's room, they were fond of spreading it like a coverlet, oblivious to the irony of smoothing "the colors of the sunset" on an elderly patient's bed. But it looked good there, and it added a homey touch. The morning she died, I arrived to find her room tidied and my mother laid out in the bed, the afghan tucked up to her chin as if keeping her warm as she slept.

Because my mother passed away in December, my father felt a sense of urgency to donate her clothing to charity in time to receive the tax deduction for 2010. After nearly sixty years of marriage, however, this impulse was balanced by the desire to cling to every scrap of their life together. Kathy helped me sort through Mom's closet, her drawers, the boxes of sweaters under the bed… and Dad kept telling us that we should just take these garments, which were several sizes too large for us and hopelessly out of date, and wear them ourselves. Kathy tactfully pointed out, "The style is just a little too old for us." "Hang onto her clothes, then," said my father, "because someday you will be old enough to wear them."

As I write this – the better part of a year since she drew her last breath – I am wearing one of my mother's nightgowns, a frilly, flowered effort that does not suit my self-image in middle age. The cotton is worn soft and nearly transparent with washing. The shirt tossed on the floor at my bedside, sweat-stained and smeared with garden dirt, is a grey synthetic number with shoulder pads; Mom probably wore it to work at some point, now I wear it over denim leggings because I imagine the outfit to look funky and youthful. Two of her rings have found permanent homes on my left hand, and I never seem to leave the house without one of her scarves around my neck. The scent of her clothes from those late days when personal hygiene was failing – fabric softener and lily-of-the-valley cologne, barely concealing something unclean – clings even after repeated washings. It swaths me in a sense that is nothing like comfort. I can't seem to let it go.

Since my mother died, I feel an overwhelming impulse to wrap my life in the material leavings of her own. I wash my hair with her shampoo, wear her clothes, spread her tablecloths on my table and set her dishes out for dinner, leaf through her photo albums, worry her memory with my questions. So when we traveled to Ecuador to

205

visit our son during his semester abroad, I packed the teal rain-jacket with a purple lining that had been Mom's favorite.

The jacket, like nearly every other aspect of her life, came with a story: never mind what coat she put on in her last few years -- her pale blue windbreaker, her boiled wool car-coat, her black parka with its velveteen collar – the slide of arm into sleeve, the wrap of warmth across the back, made every coat feel to her like a last hug from her mother (who, by the time she passed, had long forgotten her daughter). Every time my mother put on a coat she would say, "This is the jacket my mother bought me when I was moving up here" – meaning when she first left home in 1949. "My mother knew it would be cold, and she was right." (The last time I took my mother to a department store this story found a new iteration. There in the changing room she told me, "These are the underpants my mother bought me when she learned that I was moving up here." "No," I laughed, "No way, Mom." "Yes," she said, "My mother knew it would be cold. I've never had to buy new underwear since then.")

In any case, that teal and purple jacket didn't suit me at all. It was too large, no longer waterproof. A total dud. But I hadn't registered that fact on our first night in Quito, a Saturday night in the Mariscal district, known for its crazy nightlife. I have never been a "crazy nightlife" kind of person, even when I was my son's age. After a long day of travel and a late dinner, all I wanted to do was sleep. The rest of Mariscal remained awake, streets lit up and loud with sirens, motors, throngs of young people chattering and calling. In an attempt to block it all out, I pulled my mother's jacket over my head, and found myself enveloped by her scent. It was sweet and sickening. She had always dreamed of visiting Ecuador and now, in a ghostly way, she was there with me. Half a world from home, I cried myself to sleep.

Though my sister and I each take pride in having a good memory, everybody gets it wrong sometimes. My husband will never let me forget the time I told him a funny story I attributed to my brother-in-law – a story which, in fact, he himself had told to me. "Is memory property?" writes Abigail Thomas in her reflections on memoir. "If two people remember a memory differently, is one of them wrong?" Because I am slightly younger than my sister, I am probably wrong fairly often when it comes to early memories: do I actually hold these experiences in my mind, or have I heard family stories so often that I have come to visualize them? As an adult, notwithstanding my impulse to drink and forget, I think I can hold my own. I'm certain that my one foray into rug-hooking resulted in that ridiculous pillow my sister brought me.

My children were born twenty months apart, the same as my sister and me. They argue about memories as much as we do. One point upon which they have always agreed, however, is a memory from preschool of "the time Daddy brought the Big Car into the house." The "Big Car" was our second VW camper, this one with a pop-top, which we drove during the early years of their lives. My husband and I still owned that van when the kids began talking about this astonishing experience. "How did Dad get the Big Car into the house?" we would ask, and they both had the same answer: "He opened the wall, drove it in, and then he closed up the wall again." "Why did he do it?" we asked, and they answered, "Who knows? Ask him." (I like this answer: at the ages of three and five, many things adults did probably made little sense to them.) "Did you dream this?" we asked, and even to this day, as young adults, they will point to the fact that both of them remember the scene. In their minds, impossible as this memory is, it happened. They are witnesses.

Being rational parents, my husband and I concluded that our elder child must have had a dream she described so vividly to her brother it eventually became real to them both. But for them, this is a matter of memory. When my sister and I used to lie awake, listening to our parents laughing with their guests downstairs, we shared a fantasy of dropping a bucket through the bedroom floor to the dining room, magically selecting the best foods – heavy on desserts – and hauling it back up to share. I can see her in my mind's eye even now, reaching across the gap between our twin beds to hand me half a slice of chocolate cake. I thank her, taste it,

207

smack my lips, and take pleasure from how much she is enjoying the other half. Our mother's chocolate cake is perfectly delicious.

What makes a memory real? When we lose ourselves vividly in fantasy, is our memory of it not real? When we wake from dreaming with images lingering in our minds, are those images not real? When we imagine our fondest wishes, are they not real? In his rich ruminations on memory, St. Augustine wrote, "Which images we store and how they are constructed, who can tell? Though it is clear by which sense each has been brought in and put away. For even while I rest in darkness and silence, I can have my memory produce color if I wish... and though my tongue is still and my throat mute, yet I can sing as much as I wish." Memory of the senses can be as vivid as the senses themselves.

To the Ancient Greeks, Mnemosene was the mother of the Muses. A Titan, a daughter of Heaven, she represented the act of mind required to keep stories intact before the advent of literacy, hence the notion of "mnemonic devices." She personified memory. She invented language. The Greeks understood the Muses to be goddesses who inspired artistic creation, whose spirits were sources of knowledge related orally for centuries in the ancient culture, contained in poetry, music, and myth.

My mother was besotted by memory, and functioned as the keeper of all stories in the family. Before being diagnosed with Alzheimer's, she started gathering these tales into books for her grandchildren. She continued to write over a period of ten years, until the progress of the disease made it impossible for her to follow through on any extended task. When, long after she had ceased to write, we collected eleven volumes of her stories and poems in a single large book, she recognized the motifs of the stories far more than her own authorship. If I read aloud to her, she'd exclaim, "That sounds just like something my father said! How did you know that?"

The stories she wrote are my mother's greatest gift to her grandchildren. They detail her childhood, her family's history, what she knew of my father's family. She wrote in hopes of stirring the elements of her past into the future, making her memories part of her grandchildren's lives. The very acts of writing or telling imply ownership of the narrative: *This is how it happened, and this is why we should remember.*

Back to that hideous pillow, which now graces a chair in my family room: to this day, I'm not a hundred percent certain when my sister made the grand gesture of giving it to me. Were she and Kathy even in town at the same time? I know that my sister returned to New York the Sunday after Mom died. Did Kathy maybe come the following week? Am I conflating a few winter evenings when we shared a little too much wine?

In the moment, whenever it was, I respond tactfully for once. I see the wisdom of acknowledging someone else's memory without challenging its accuracy. "Thank you," I say to my sister, and I am speaking from my heart. "This means a lot to me."

If You Live Long Enough

Autumn, 2011

This time of year in the Midwest shines with the goodness of life. August slouches lazily into September. The days are clear, the nights cool and fine for sleeping; the wind off Lake Michigan tangles in tree tops, tossing down the first scatter of dry leaves and rattling our old windows in their frames. Every time I return from garden to kitchen with a basket of tomatoes, orange and red peppers, bunches of thyme and oregano, I give thanks.

In past years, this was also a season of anxiety in our house. The weather changes fast. When thermometer and barometer fluctuated in tandem, our old dogs started to fret. The spectacular thunderstorms unleashed every now and then to cool summer down to fall sent the dogs into a frenzy of worry, pacing and panting, scratching at our faces and waking us with their pungent hyperventilation. When Jackie died a few years ago, Boo became even more phobic about storms, as if to carry on the tradition for a fallen friend.

A neighbor rang the doorbell today, and as I went to greet him I thought, "My house is not supposed to be quiet." For the past dozen years, every arrival was met with a hearty chorus of barking as the dogs converged on the front hall in a tangle of tails, legs, and noses. Today only Curtis is left--the dog that seldom even bothers to rise from the couch to see who's there. Opening the door, saying hello in a low, uninterrupted voice, I felt desolate and wrong.

Boo, the dog of my heart, died two weeks ago. Perhaps it's false to phrase that so naturally: she died because the vet, at my request, slipped a catheter into a vein in her right front leg and pumped in a sedative, followed by a drug that stopped her great old heart from beating. After months of endlessly increasing pain, anxiety, and confusion my dear old Boo lay in my arms, basking in the comfort of one last hug, munching on the kind of cheap, junky treats that she loved but I refused to buy for her. At last her head slumped and she peacefully let go. A thirteen year old neighbor,

210

barely starting her life at the same age Boo passed from it, left a handmade and beautifully over-written card in my mailbox: "I am so sorry to hear that Boo finally had to let go of this earthly paradise that you so caringly provided...."

Two weeks, and the household is adjusting to a simpler rhythm. As an only-dog, Curtis enjoys the extra attention, though he sometimes seems as lost as I feel without Boo. It's for the best, I tell myself. We did everything we could. When she could no longer climb stairs, we took to sleeping downstairs in the guest bed. That was eight months ago. When she could no longer rest at night, I got up repeatedly to comfort her. Eventually, she took to staying outside all night, which made me so anxious I barely slept at all. Boo was old, and the pain in her back and legs had gone beyond managing with medications. She knew how much we loved her, didn't she? It's for the best, isn't it?

There were many times during the last weeks of my mother's life when my thoughts careened frighteningly close to prayer. The act of prayer itself is not what unsettles me: although raised to eschew religion and chronically incapable of joining any organized group, I have learned, through the decades, to find my own center, to embrace awe, to give thanks wholeheartedly, to speak to and about forces far larger than myself. What scared me was to find my prayerful thoughts shifting from expressions of appreciation to pleas for a particular gift. That "gift" was my mother's death. After making sure that Verna was set to sit by Mom through the night, I'd retreat to the acute care lounge at Morana Hospital, rest my forehead against the floor-to-ceiling windows with the whole twilit city spread out at my feet – the vast darkness of Lake Michigan, the daisy chain of lights down the East Side, the shadowed ribbon of the Milwaukee River floodplain where my dogs and I have greeted countless mornings, the taverns of Riverwest, the unabashed brilliance of downtown, neighborhoods revealing themselves in glittering grids to the south and west – I would gaze at all of those lights, at all of that life, and sob till tears running down the glass blurred my view. "Please let her go," I murmured, some nights a hundred times, "Please let her go."

I don't know who or what I was praying to. The words snuck up on me unbidden when I had finally calmed my mother down enough to rest or to eat a spoonful of soup. They blindsided me in the hospital elevator, surrounded by strangers, each of whom carried a private weight of grief or a secret hope. They distracted me on the rare days I made it to work. "Please let her go."

Was I selfish? Perhaps. Though I wanted an end to her suffering, I also wanted to return to my own life: I had not changed address, job, or marital status, but I missed my husband, my work, my home. I was doing my best as a daughter and caregiver, and I never was able to do much good. Mom was lost in paranoia, increasingly unable to recognize her closest family: what did she have left of her life and herself? However much I sat with her, said soothing words, sang songs, held her hands, kissed her when she'd let me, I could not bring her back. I could not help her make sense of the jumbled mess of her thoughts, which scattered and clumped like decades of leaf litter underfoot. She was drifting away, and all the love in the world could not help me keep her with me. I was exhausted. I wanted to know that this would not, could not go on forever. There was nothing I could do to ease her inevitable passing but murmur my guilty prayers.

One of my Irish cousins regularly forwards "clever" emails to everyone on his list. He's a very sweet guy, and ingenuous enough not to notice that this kind of well-intentioned spamming can wear on the receivers.

While Mom was in the hospital (which he did not know at the time), one of his forwards concerned health care. The gist of it was this: Two middle-aged patients go to the doctor with back pain; after the fact, we can be sure that they have the same complaint. Patient A requires further testing, which takes a month or two to complete. Upon receipt of the results, Patient A's doctor arranges for a follow-up appointment, provides a referral to a surgeon, and the surgery is completed within six months of the first appointment. Patient B also requires further testing, which is completed that same day. Based upon the results, Patient B's doctor contacts a specialist and arranges for surgery within thirty-six hours. Bear in mind that the prognosis is dimmer with every day that surgery is delayed.

The punch line is that Patient A is an average workingman with a family, while Patient B is a golden retriever. I don't know much about the Irish health care system, but the commentary is clear. For whatever it's worth, he forwarded this to cousins who live in England and Canada, as well as to me.

How would – how *does* – an ordinary person effectively connect with appropriate healthcare in the United States these days? I keep dwelling on how well my parents prepared for the depredations of age and infirmity. They had health insurance to supplement Medicare, long-term care insurance, more than adequate savings for retirement. They were stakeholders in a retirement community that provided nursing home care on the premises. They had education, money in the bank, family support, and careful planning behind them. They had resources at their disposal that most people in this country cannot afford.

And all of this failed my mother at the end. Hospitalized in a state of the art facility, she was cared for by highly trained nurses who seemed ill equipped to handle a patient with Alzheimer's. She was medicated haphazardly. The geriatric psychiatrist overseeing her care never bothered to conceal his lack of patience for my father and his questions, or the futility of his efforts to bring my mother's behavior back into the range of "normal." My mother's suffering was best understood by a handful of aides in the nursing home and the hospice staff that visited her in the last two weeks of her life. The degree of effective compassion she received from caregivers sometimes seemed to be in inverse proportion to the level of their education and income.

When my mother died, she was very old and her pain had gone beyond managing. Somewhere inside, I hope that she still knew how much we loved her. I prayed to let her go. My life is far too quiet now, but it's for the best, isn't it?

213

On a September evening nine months after my mother passed away, two weeks after Boo died, I am putting by two dozen half-pints of raspberry jam and listening to an NPR interview with Jane Gross, author of *A Bittersweet Season*. "We all think that we'll just be playing tennis one day and then dead the next," she says, "but thanks to medical technology there is a longer and longer time between being *fine* and death." Dipping the hot jam into jars in the steamy kitchen, I feel myself break into a different kind of sweat. I know that in-between time, that limbo "between being *fine* and death." My mother walked there for years, and I tried my best to walk beside her. It was a time of mistakes and missteps, grievance and grief. I cannot name it, and I do not relish the prospect of dwelling there long when I am old.

I am reminded of a story my father told me years ago: a man he knew, a distinguished scientist, travelled to Russia to receive an award for his life's work. While in Moscow, he was invited to the Bolshoi Ballet. The curtain rose: the dancers swirled, all gauze and muscle, through onrushing streams of music, bodies curving like bird wings. At least that's how I imagine it, having seen the Bolshoi as a child.

At intermission, the scientist exchanged pleasantries with his hosts then appeared to doze off. The performance resumed. When the last chord died, when the last ovation faded, when the lights came up on ladies wrapping themselves in shawls and gentlemen buttoning overcoats, he did not wake up. I imagine the gradual escalation of concern: a tap on the shoulder, a shake of the arm, imprecations whispered in the ear, shouts for assistance... sometime during the performance, he had died.

My father no longer remembers telling me this. In fact, he no longer remembers the person the story is about. When I asked him about it recently, he said I must have made it up. My memory, however, holds particulars so vivid that I went online to seek corroboration. The outline of the story holds: my father knew a man who died silently, peacefully, at the peak of his career, awash

214

in a tide of pellucid music rushing between downbeat and final cadence.

My father was sixty-four years old when this happened. The scientist (who died in Leningrad, not Moscow; during a concert, not a ballet) was slightly younger. No doubt he planned to grow old, to welcome grandchildren and great-grandchildren, to live as long as my mother lived. But, as departures go, his was definitely a class act.

It's easy to forget that growing old is a privilege, not a given. Karma, fortune, love and prayer notwithstanding, there's little we can count on. Like most people, I hope to live long even though my family history suggests that it's likely I will develop Alzheimer's disease. More than once, as my mother declined, I told my husband that I'd rather die than dwell as long as she did with dementia: he pointed out that by the time I am as far gone as she was, I will no longer be capable of deciding to take my own life. But I mean this seriously. Not one of my beloved dogs has suffered to the last breath; my mother did. Given the choice, do I need to draw the last possible breath that fate accords me?

Tonight, I'm inhaling the healthy steam of next season's preserves, a promise of bounty, and feeling grateful to have made it this far. If you live long enough, you begin to accept the fact that precious parts of life are simply behind you; you learn to live with the loss of people who gave your life meaning in the first place. By the end of my mother's long life, nearly everyone she remembered was dead, and only my father, my sister and I remained to mourn her. Even so, her absence sometimes seems bigger to me than my presence. I've reached an age where, when I talk to myself, a chorus of ghosts accompanies my voice. This bittersweet time of year, my mother's voice echoes loudest and purest of all.

215

Day of Infamy

On December 7, 2011, I invite my father to lunch. He telephones three times during the morning because he cannot remember when I will pick him up (noon), a pattern of compulsive time-checking that he relies upon more and more as his short-term memory falters. Over lunch, I observe that it is Pearl Harbor Day and he fixes me with a disappointed scowl: "Don't you remember that this is also the day your mother passed away?"

Of course I remember. I have been thinking of nothing else all week, wondering how or whether to broach the subject with him. Aside from his congenital discomfort with emotion, I worry about his increasing confusion and forgetfulness: would he recognize the date, I wondered, as the anniversary of Mom's death? If he forgot, wouldn't it be better to let the oversight slide and hold my mother in my own heart?

After lunch, I kiss my father goodbye and drive to Chicago to meet my husband. Dad phones four times during my two hours on the road, anxious to confirm whether I will be away tonight or tomorrow night. Though he refuses assistance, he clearly relies on me to stay close by to visit with him five or six times a week. My father's temperament is reclusive. My gregarious mother was his bridge to the world, and I inherited her outgoing nature: when I'm not visiting he is entirely alone.

December seventh: the anniversary of both Pearl Harbor Day and my mother's death. And that certainly isn't all. On December 7, 2006, for example, two months after my parents moved to Umbria Court, I answered the phone to hear a voice I did not recognize explaining that my father had been rushed to the hospital: he had gone to see a doctor for a minor problem, and then passed out in the waiting room, hitting his head. They took him to the ER. My mother was still sitting there, confused and growing increasingly agitated, and no one quite knew what to do with her.

My daughter had arrived home for the holidays two days earlier, at the end of her first semester of college. Suddenly I was barking orders at her as I rushed out the door: take care of this, take care of that, call so and so, mind the dogs, and I will be in touch later to let you know when I'll be back. I have no doubt that someday in the future she will have to ditch her family to run to my side for an entirely avoidable emergency... My apologies in advance.

I picked up my mother and we hurried to the hospital. Dad was lucid, if dazed. The day crept by with a smorgasbord of tests, all results inconclusive. As night fell, my father was admitted for observation, and my mother released into my care.

At this point in her dementia, Mom had not yet shown signs of a serious inclination to wander. Besides, it was cold and dark outside, so I felt sure she'd stay put in the lobby while I dashed to the parking structure to retrieve the car. As I drew into the semi-circular drive, I saw her pitching unsteadily out through automatic doors towards a taxi-van for disabled passengers, her left hand waving warmly at the driver as her right hand reached for the door handle. I opened the window, called out. Her head jerked in my direction and she nearly stumbled. "You're always so loud," she remarked, as I came to her side and guided her towards my car.

I didn't feel much like talking on the drive home. Between my father's anxiety and my mother's badgering ("Where are we? Why are we here? Where are we?"), between the glacial pace of hospital testing and the rapid-fire calls to my workplace to cover my absence, it had been a trying day. It was long past dark, and I still had to fix dinner for my mother, get her to bed, and settle down to sleep on the sofa because she couldn't be left alone; my classes started at nine-thirty the next morning, so I'd have to get her up and dressed before leaving her in the care of my eighteen year old daughter for the day.

"What day is this?" my mother asked suddenly, and I muttered, "Tuesday."

"No, the date."

"December seventh."

"It's Pearl Harbor Day. FDR called this 'the day that will live in infamy.'"

217

Impressed that she had made the connection, I asked Mom what she remembered from Pearl Harbor Day. "I slept a little late that morning," she told me, "and when I got up and went into the kitchen I turned on the television." I began to interrupt but she talked right over me, her voice heavy in the dark. "I didn't usually turn it on during the day, but that morning I did. And it was awful: I watched live news coverage of Japanese bombers crossing the Pacific. They were right there on radar, and you just knew what was coming, but there was nothing anyone could do. Then they showed everything blowing up. I ran out of the kitchen and told my husband, 'There's going to be a war.'"

How could I respond? Besides the lack of TV in 1941, there was no warning of the attack, no radar tracking, no live news coverage. On Pearl Harbor Day, my mother was sixteen, halfway through her junior year at Bayside High.

I related this conversation to my husband that night, and he asked, "Was she really talking about Pearl Harbor?" I caught his train of thought immediately: there was a different morning on which my mother must have turned on the TV and learned that the country was under attack with no warning – September 11, 2001. Watching those hijacked planes smash into the towers, her heart must have frozen. I'm certain she rushed from the kitchen to tell her husband, "There's going to be a war."

It's a quaint truism that every generation has its touchstone event, its "day that will live in infamy," the moment in time that you can point to and ask "Where were you when...?" knowing that everyone in the room can readily provide a detailed answer. For my parents, Pearl Harbor Day stood like a cairn leading them back into thickets of thorny and sometimes heroic memory. The fallout from that attack ravaged their generation. There was no longer the option of staying neutral: within four days, the US was officially at war with both Japan and Germany.

For people of my age, most anyone could tell you where he or she was on the day of JFK's assassination. I was in Miss D'Amanda's first grade classroom gluing a Thanksgiving collage when the principal rushed in and dismissed school for the rest of the day; then I was dashing wildly around the playground, desperate to locate my big sister in the crowd of children pouring out of #23 School. Our mother was fond of recalling that I cried because Caroline and John-John had lost their Daddy.

For my own children, the touchstone is 9/11. They walked to school on a dazzling autumn morning, and just as classes began the towers crumbled. My daughter, then twelve years old, remembers crying with fear for her cousins in Manhattan; my son, who was only ten, recalls his surprise that buildings could blow up anywhere besides Oklahoma City. They and their contemporaries will be swapping these stories for years.

Every day is a collection of stories worth swapping. One of my colleagues who married on September 11, 1977, brought an album of wedding photos to show her students on September 12, 2001. They giggled at her daisy crown, her flowered dress, her husband in his wide lapels and John Lennon glasses, as she quietly reminded them that life goes on, that at any given moment both good and bad things are happening in the world, that it's important to embrace the full range of our experience as human beings. This is a message I take to heart. On my husband's thirty-fifth birthday, he lost his father to cancer, but he and his mother still celebrate the day. Every day, after all, is an anniversary of births and deaths, triumph and catastrophe, not to mention completely pedestrian events. It is up to each of us to curse – or to redeem – the days that add up to our lives.

As a child, my faulty grasp of history and my inclination not to listen carefully often led me to confusion. For years, I could have sworn that my mother told me a story about bicycling in New England, staying at youth hostels with her sorority sisters from Queens College, as the Japanese attacked Pearl Harbor. As I recalled the story, she heard nothing of the attack until she returned to New York a week later. At some point it dawned on me that in 1941 my mother was still in High School, and that nobody in their right mind would set out to bicycle through Vermont in December.

I had two stories crossed: my mother was hostelling with the gals from Alpha Omega when the atom bomb was dropped on Hiroshima, August 6, 1945, another touchstone day in my parents' lives.

The day the Bomb dropped, my father was on a troopship somewhere in the Pacific. His company had recently come back from Europe, the first relatively intact unit to sail into New York Harbor after VE Day, welcomed by fire hoses and barges full of dancing girls. Cheering from the top deck of the Staten Island Ferry, my mother unknowingly witnessed her future husband's return.

Then, after two-weeks,' leave and a bit of training, they set out across the Pacific, prepared to land on Japanese-held Islands, possibly in Japan itself. Their training had included viewing footage from Normandy, wave after wave of GI's storming the beach to be mowed down before reaching dry ground; nobody needed to say that the outlook was easily as bleak for them. Miraculously, halfway to Japan, the convoy diverted to the Philippines.

My mother was fond of telling us that Dad was saved by the atom bomb. How was I, as a child, to reckon this equation? My father was at the center of my world; without him, I would not even exist. The atom bomb killed over 200,000 people in Hiroshima and Nagasaki. Over 200,000 people.

Once Mom returned from the hospital to Cascia Hall, I returned to work with a vengeance, grateful for the distraction of classes, advising, faculty meetings, complete immersion in other people's concerns. Diminished as my mother was, I believed our family might return to some measure of equilibrium. On Monday, December sixth I was in the classroom from noon to seven P.M. Around four, a familiar face appeared in the doorway – it was Bryn, a spunky, unforgettable former student who had confided in me throughout her senior year, a time made turbulent by conflicts with her major professor. She had been a delight to teach, and I was always glad to hear from her.

When Bryn showed up, I was reconvening class after a break, so all I could do was step out into the corridor to give her a quick hug. "Can you come for dinner when my class ends?" I asked. We drove home together, cooked and ate, celebrated the signing of her first book contract, and drank enough that it wasn't safe for her to drive two hours home, so I insisted that she stay. Bryn borrowed an old flannel nightgown from me and settled in my son's room.

With Mom out of the hospital, my husband and I were growing happily re-accustomed to sleeping through the night. The change had less to do with Mom's condition than with the response of her caregivers. Back at Cascia Hall the staff, of necessity, took the crazy jive of dementia in stride. The drama of hospitalization subsided: my mother was medicated in a timely and stress-free way, and nobody got upset if she was frightened or loud. The aides understood that it mattered less *who* interacted with Mom than *how* they interacted, an insight lost upon the hospital nurses when they dialed my number every midnight.

But this night was not to be peaceful. When the phone rang at five-thirty in the morning, I struck out groggily and knocked it off the bedside table. Bringing the receiver to my ear, I heard a woman's voice calling, "Hello? Hello?" "Hello," I grumbled. "Is this Vivian Harway's daughter Judith?" she asked. The formality startled me awake. "Yes." "I'm so sorry, but your mother passed away between five and five-fifteen."

I must have said something – "My mother…" "Dear God…" "Please, no…" "Oh, shit…." My husband understood without being told. We got up, dressed quickly, headed for the car. Then I remembered: what about Bryn, our accidental guest?

Our daughter was also at home that night, though she had come in after the rest of us went to bed. I slipped a note under her door, knowing that I'd be calling earlier than she'd like to wake: "Sweetie, Dad and I are with Grandma. Not good news. Bryn stayed over last night: please offer her my apologies and a good breakfast. I will call her later as well."

I imagine the two of them meeting that morning in the kitchen…

221

Daughter: You must be Bryn.
Bryn: Yes. I've heard a lot about you.
Daughter: Mom's not here, but she left a message. I think my grandmother maybe died this morning.
Bryn: I'm so sorry. She said.... Oh, I'm just so sorry.
Daughter: Thanks. I'll know more when Mom calls, but I kind of know now. It's been such a hard time. Can I get you a cup of coffee? A bagel?

My mother would have appreciated the clumsy poetry of this scene: two beautiful, and completely different young women navigating choppy waters together, each trying to set aside her own distress and confusion to put the other at ease. My mother would have taken comfort in the fact that life goes on, that they shared the blessing of a good breakfast to start a day that will ever burn in my memory.

To Dust You Shall Return

"I've told my children that when I die, to release balloons in the sky to celebrate..."

-- Elisabeth Kubler-Ross

"Tell me," my father says, resting his hand on my arm, "do you know where your mother's ashes are right now?"

I am caught off guard. Of course I know. He has them. They are in a cardboard box on top of his dresser, less than twenty feet from the sofa where we sit as this conversation unfolds.

But, contrary to my assumption, his memory is not the problem. "It's just a box," he explains. "It says nothing. Maybe we should stick a label on it."

Tears well in my eyes. "But Daddy, you said...." Then I think better of it and shut up. He said lots of things before and after Mom's death, things he meant as comfort to us, and they all dissolve into what he says now: "Of course, it won't change anything."

Eight months earlier, after filling out my mother's death certificate, the hospice nurse handed me the business card of a funeral home a few blocks from my house. It's directly across the street from the elementary school my kids attended, facing the crosswalk where I taught them to look both ways and try to make eye contact with drivers to be sure they see you. It's kitty-corner from the firehouse, behind the public library. I had walked past it literally thousands of times without noticing it was there.

And what a peculiar call to make. "Hello. My mother just died. I'm looking for someone to handle her body," I said, struck by how lame and matter-of-fact my words sounded. I didn't want anyone to handle her body. In the four hours between her death and that call, I had already come to realize that I didn't want to handle it myself. It was no longer the unresponsive but familiar body I had embraced and kissed and wept over when I arrived that morning, the diminished body I had tried to lift into one last hug, the body from which I had come; the face was graying, and the flesh cooling

223

as though packed with ice. It was no longer *her* body. It was something she had left behind. I did not want it near me, and I did not want anyone to take it away.

We met with the funeral director later that afternoon, around the same time his staff collected my mother from the nursing home. He worked hard to keep the mood light, running through a series of jokes so sappy we laughed out of pity. "Look at my Pride and Joy," he crowed, opening his wallet to show us photos of two brands of dish soap. *My mother died today*, I thought, seething; my father, ever the gentleman, validated this idiotic patter with quiet nods and grins. Then there was the infernal jargon of the profession: what *final repose* might we desire for her *cremains?*

My sister and I exchanged glances and rolled our eyes. Dad looked down and fidgeted: on this, the worst day he'd ever faced, a stranger expected him to hurry into a decision about what to do with what remained of the love of his life. I had already voiced my objections to embalming and burial, hoping that my revulsion would reinforce Dad's inclination toward cremation. Then my sister spoke. "You know," she said, evoking a circle of friends with whom my parents had shared the happiest summers of the happiest years of their lives, "Rose and Lynn sprinkled their husbands in the lake on Cape Cod."

Dad brightened. Cremation it was. He chose the plainest container for Mom's ashes. The funeral director assured my father that the simple cardboard box would be no extra cost, though the charge for it on the bill we eventually received was $170.

My mind dials back to when my oldest dog died a few years ago, and I asked the vet how we would know that the ashes returned to us from the crematorium were hers. I trust this vet: I've known him for fifteen years, he's cared for all of our pets, and he gave my daughter her first job. His answer came with a shrug: "We've never had any complaints." Because Jackie, the dog, was a passionate swimmer, my kids waded out into Lake Michigan in April, a freezing proposition, tossing those dear ashes we assumed to be hers to the wind and waves.

224

And now, on my father's dresser, there's this cardboard box. "Do you like the idea of a label?" he asks. "Don't you think we should let future generations know what's in here?" He's had second thoughts about scattering her ashes, and who can blame him? It won't change anything.

About a year before we became parents, my husband and I traveled the Canadian tundra by canoe with a small group led by a wildlife biologist. We had big dreams and little sense of how arduous the trip might be. Driving over forty-eight hours from Milwaukee to Fort Smith, I was stricken with a stomach bug that we wishfully misread as morning sickness. Our fifth anniversary passed on the road, frequently parking our 1973 VW van on the shoulder so I could vomit into ditches choked by lupine and fireweed. At last we found ourselves camped beside a crystalline lake in Wood Buffalo National Park, breathlessly watching a flock of sand-hill cranes graze a marshy meadow, hoping that the wooziness which dogged our steps on solid ground – definitely flu, now that we both were afflicted – might pass before next morning when we'd lash our canoes to the pontoons of a couple of floatplanes and fly north.

Once aloft, my discomfort was compounded by the fact that my husband and I had boarded different aircraft. From a porthole of that single-engine Otter, I watched the infinity of the arctic landscape rolling out below, the scanty, haggard trees of the taiga dwindling to endless tundra. My teeth chattered with the plane's vibration. The delicate white wings which carried my husband glistened like a tiny cross against a dark, water-pocked land that had nothing to hide. How, I wondered, could that miniature X mark the spot where the most important person in my life drifted improbably through air?

The planes touched down, side by side, on a broad expanse of water. Anywhere else, this would have qualified as a lake, but as August dawns, high arctic rivers spread across flat reaches of permafrost in endless oxbows and vast, meandering pools that vary crazily in depth. We splashed into shallows at the edge of twenty pellucid acres, our first introduction to the river we were to paddle for the next two weeks.

I remember each of our companions on that trip with affection, but the one who returns to my thoughts most vividly is Carl, a sweet, guileless man with a goofy sense of humor. Once, as my husband and I strained to catch up after detouring to explore, we heard his voice singing out across choppy water: "It's Beetlebaum!" Easily twenty-five years my senior, Carl was protective of me to the point of chivalry and took great delight in making me laugh.

Carl was the first mortician I had ever met. His father started a small-town funeral home, and he grew up helping out behind the scenes, eventually taking over the family business. "Isn't that awfully depressing work?" I asked, and he shook his head: "It's wonderful. It's all about people. I work with folks when they are most in need, and I love being able to help."

My curiosity piqued, I peppered Carl with questions, like an anthropologist gathering data on an unfamiliar culture. He answered with endless patience, explaining the process of embalming and the psychology of open casket funerals, both of which I found mystifying and creepy; sometimes his eyes misted up as he recollected the grief of particular clients.

During one of our conversations Carl told me a strange, apocryphal story about a corpse being exhumed after five years to ascertain how it was holding up. It's possible that this was an urban legend, but I found myself riveted by the weird details: because the body had been embalmed and "laid to rest" within a high quality casket, it was well preserved and completely recognizable, the only blemish being some mold growing on the face. Then he laughed and remarked that most embalming jobs would not look so great five years out: unless the casket had a remarkable seal, vermin and moisture would get in, and the resulting decay might take a little longer but would be no more lovely than leaving a body to the natural bacteria that cause it to swell with gas and turn the flesh all runny. "Death isn't pretty," he said, "but if folks want to think that Grandpa will always look the way they remember him, that's OK by me."

I dream it is the day after my mother died and I am soon to leave on a long trip. My sister and I live together, and our father is not in the picture. We cannot decide what to do with Mom's body, so we opt to delay: at some point in the future we'll bury or cremate her, but for now we keep her in a basin of water. It looks like Sleeping Beauty's glass coffin, although this one has tinted glass to be more discreet. We set it in the kitchen before the window, and there Mom lies.

We frequently check on her – neither one of us wants to look directly, so we take turns peeking at her head, hoping that nothing is changing. The glass is dark, the water is dark, the only change we note is that Mom's head seems to be growing dark as well. I depart.

A jumble of scenes unfolds: I'm staying in a rooming house with lawns sloping down to a beach, driving with my husband up and down the lakefront, trying to coax my dog to swim…. Water links all these diversions.

Then my sister and I are at home again. She introduces me to an odd little woman, jittery as a squirrel, who apparently has been living in our house while we were away. She whispers to me that this woman has looked at Mom, adding ominously, "We left this too long."

I rush to my mother's glass casket. The water roils with bubbles, gases escaping her body and rising in great boiling columns. The body is almost obscured by turbulent, turbid water. Feeling sick to my stomach, I crouch and sniff the outside of the glass.

We are desperate to be rid of this mess. We place several calls, but no one can help us until the following spring. Finally, a man in a white coat offers to keep my mother's corpse in a line of others that rest in an infinitely long vault the height and width of a coffin. When it's time to retrieve her, he says, he will draw out the whole line of bodies like the drawer of a card catalog, and give us her link in the chain. I point out that decay has already made her unrecognizable. "Don't worry," he tells us, "We always keep track of the sequence."

In the dream we never reach a decision, but we haul the glass coffin outside under a tree. It can't stay in the house any longer. Besides, Mom was happiest out in the garden.

The other day, my father asked me again about the label for Mom's ashes. Again he said "so that future generations will know what's in there." Why keep ashes lying around the house in a cardboard box for future generations? For that matter, why try to preserve a body from natural decay? If we believe that the essence of the person departs at death, that the soul departs, why worry about the remains at all?

I didn't know until I looked it up that strict Jewish tradition does not condone embalming: because the body contains a soul which is due back to its creator at the moment of death, Jews bury their dead within twenty-four hours to make good on a sacred debt. Embalming prevents the body from returning to its source ("for dust you are and to dust you will return"); for similar reasons, cremation is unacceptable.

Faced with the question of what to do with my mother's body, however, tradition and law never had much purchase. My father, skeptical of religion and fearful of emotion, favored a no-fuss approach. This jibed with my own disdain for euphemism. I grew up among Catholic playmates who were told, "Your puppy has gone to sleep," or "Grandma is resting in the arms of Jesus." Even in first grade, though, I knew a lie when I heard one: the puppy had been flattened by a truck, and Grandma was resting underground in the cemetery. According to Elisabeth Kubler-Ross, the ground-breaking thanatologist who described and named five stages of grief, "the elaborate expensive display of an open casket with all the makeup... enforces the belief that the person is only asleep, and ... would only help to prolong the stage of denial."

The last evening we spent on Wolf River, Carl broke out a big flask of Johnnie Walker hidden in his pack and passed it around. There was a sense of pride in our circle: we had put many miles of tricky water behind us, dogged by heavy winds and rain; we had scouted for wolf dens, tracked caribou, laid side by side beneath green curtains of aurora; we had grown close and comfortable in one another's company. My husband and I took some friendly ribbing about our fallacious assumption that we had started a pregnancy at the start of the trip, and everyone made us promise to write as soon as we actually became expectant parents. We ran through all the inside jokes we had accumulated in sixteen days of isolation, and toasted our commitment to keep in touch.

All good intentions aside, life is a process of separation: after a few years of exchanging cards, we lost track of these dear people. If Carl is still alive, he must be nearly eighty. In the years since we paddled together across the tundra, the only other funeral director I've ever met is the sleaze-ball we entrusted with my mother's body, a fact which makes my memory of Carl more precious today: I know he would have honored my wish to let go, as well as my father's need to hold fast to an unlabeled cardboard box full of ashes.

What is left of my mother's body, then, is a carton of chalky grey dust that I trust has something to do with her flesh, with her being. Although she was raised to believe in a cloud called Heaven, a place so perfect the dead would give thanks for dying, she taught her own daughters to cherish the here and now, to love life on this earth because it is all we've got. That's why, when I imagine Heaven, it looks much like the tundra: pristine and windswept, lined with caribou trails and pocked by wolf dens in the lee of eskers. The face of eternity is frozen and flowing at once, its waters sustaining flocks of snow geese and teeming with arctic char. The light is relentless, so clear that when you look downstream you can see into tomorrow, where low-bush berries ripen vividly towards autumn. It is a landscape that owes nothing whatever to man.

Now and at the Hour of Our Death

A year and a day after my mother died, when Jewish tradition dictates that family members re-emerge from a period of grief and begin to engage fully with life once again, my father asked for help finding Mom's Christmas card list in the chaos of his apartment. Together, he and I would keep up a custom she had single-handedly maintained throughout the decades of their marriage. As a child, I delighted in assisting her, laboring over the cursive of every address, always writing "Mr. and Mrs. (or Dr. and Mrs.) John Doe," with old-fashioned formality intact. My mother composed a note inside each card and signed it, but I had the privilege of licking stamps and running a damp sponge over envelope flaps to seal them. If I did anything even slightly messy, I had to start over, because holiday cards must look perfect so our far-flung loved ones can see how much they mean to us.

In the last decade of my mother's life her frustration grew, her attention span shrank, and I became her secretary once again. In time I gratefully yielded this role to my daughter. Because she was a grandchild, it never mattered that her penmanship was erratic or that she insistently acknowledged both partners in a couple by first name: by then my mother could barely manage to sign the cards, let alone write a personal note of remembrance inside.

A year and a day after my mother died, searching through cupboards in my father's study, I discovered a collection of Mom's travel diaries. Like her, I keep a journal whenever I find myself in an unfamiliar environment (once, in Nicaragua, I was asked to stop writing because I was making people nervous: recording what others said or did was a serious matter in a country that had known years of tyranny). Paging through the first of Mom's diaries that came to hand, I recognized my own tendency toward overly assiduous observation, as though writing made memory real and tangible, transferable to an imagined posterity.

With not a word to my father, I stuffed the notebooks into my purse and sneaked them away. Later, I phoned my sister. "Thank goodness you took them," she said, "If Dad knew they existed he'd

put them in a 'safe place' and we'd never see them again."
England, '69; Switzerland, '86; Spain, '89; Costa Rica, '90;
Venezuela, '96... I had unearthed lost treasure.

In among my mother's travel journals was a 4"x 6" spiral
notebook with a light blue cover, the title centered prominently in
her low, loopy cursive:

Reflections on the Death of My Mother

July 30, 1985 (the first entry reads) –

> *At 2:36 this morning, I became an orphan. My poor
> gallant mother gave up the fight after struggling for life
> since that awful accident in June when she sustained a
> closed head injury.... A closed head injury is dangerous at
> any age. The body can't handle it at age eighty-four. The
> blood supply for the brain is not as ample at eighty-four as
> at forty-four, and when there is internal swelling and
> bleeding in the intra-cranial spaces, the healing substances
> in the fresh new blood cannot circulate as easily.
> Encephalopathy results, and stroke, and progressive loss of
> function.*

I felt a chill down my spine: this passage could have described
my mother's condition after falling on November 3, 2010. Though
an MRI was done before her admission to the hospital, cranial
trauma clearly accelerated her decline; there was no such thing as
an MRI when my grandmother hit her head, so doctors must have
relied on x-rays and guesswork. No one used the word
"encephalopathy" in the last weeks of my mother's life, or
speculated upon whether she might have suffered small strokes:
because of her Alzheimer's diagnosis, all other explanations for
her deterioration seemed irrelevant.

It pains me to admit that when my mother's mother passed, I
was not paying attention. That was the summer my husband and I
had flown to Vancouver to collect the 1973 VW van from his
parents. For our belated honeymoon, we dawdled through the

Canadian Rockies, loving the silence and not going out of our way to phone home on our rare forays into town.

Shouldering big packs, we set out into the backcountry. As my grandmother lay dying, we joyfully slogged across broad alluvial plains, forded rivers of glacial run-off, slept in beds of edelweiss. When, a few days out on the trail, a swollen stream forced us to turn back below Moose Pass, my husband and I retreated to the van. We spent the next week walking ridges pocked with fossils of Devonian sea-life, dipping in lakes of glacial melt-water, stargazing in the lucent nights of the northern Canadian Rockies. If I thought about my mother's mother at all, it must have been with vague concern; when I learned of her death, having called my folks from a payphone in Jasper a few days after the fact, I felt sad but distracted. It was a blistering hot evening, and all around the valley lightning ignited wildfires on the slopes. Cradling the receiver against my shoulder, I paid as much attention to the procession of helicopters dipping their crazy bags of water from mountain lakes as I did to my mother's voice. The world around me, all glistening peaks and precipices, valleys blazed by sinuous meanders of water, the sunset reddened by smoke – this world seemed vivid, real, and infinitely distant from the world of my grandmother. Distant, too, from my mother. "Don't worry," Mom sighed. Once again I had failed to measure up. "Of course you can't come home. Just enjoy your trip."

> *It was terrible* (Mom wrote of her mother's last weeks) *to see function give way to weakness and to gradually fade away. In the beginning, my mother's doctor, who will never win any prizes for medical skill or for medical humanity, scolded her for 'not trying.' He seemed to be among the last to recognize that the centers which control... complex behaviors were not working properly. So this dragged on for nearly two months, and finally, she stopped fighting, her strong heart gave in.*

Again, I felt a chill. Mom's description of her mother's doctor mirrored my feelings about Dr. Z, that he would "never win any prizes for medical skill or for medical humanity." The difference, however, was that I had long since accepted "that the centers which control... complex behaviors were not working properly" in my mother's brain, where she still held out hope that her own mother might recover. I am riveted by the remark that "this dragged on for nearly two months" – from the date of my grandmother's accident to her death, just over fifty days elapsed, the same amount of time my mother had left to live after her move to Cascia Hall.

Mom's journal continues,

> *She always said that she really believed that when she died she would promptly go to where she could be with all the people whom she loved and who loved her, and they would be waiting to greet her. These would include Dad (my* grandfather*), her parents, her three brothers and two sisters, and her grandparents – all of whom preceded her; she was very comforted by this belief.*
>
> *Last night after my sister called, I composed myself and tried to get back to sleep. I said ten Hail Mary's, because I knew Mom would expect me to, and those old reflexes do not die – 'Pray for us sinners, now and at the hour of our death, Amen.' As I was drifting off to sleep a wonderful feeling of elation engulfed me – I was happy for her, and I was happy because I knew, at that moment, that she had not just found peace but she was happy, according to her own beliefs...*

There are parts of this journal I cannot read without tears. Because she raised us in a secular home, with cursory nods to both Jewish and Catholic tradition, the image of my mother lying awake beside her staunchly atheistic husband as she said ten Hail Mary's to ease her own mother's passage into the hereafter breaks my heart. "Old reflexes do not die," however: as her non-believing,

233

rational, skeptical child I share her longing for the sacred. By admitting her spiritual need, my mother gained a measure of comfort that my father may never find. However much he loved her, he could not allow himself to mourn her openly, to pray for her, to perform any rituals that might have reaffirmed the bond they shared.

In this notebook, my mother dwelled upon both mortality and love:

> *Coming into the world in the twenties and growing up in the thirties and during WWII (all pre-penicillin), I knew a lot about death as a child. Many family members died. Many of my friends lost parents to death. It was almost unheard of to know a child from a home broken by divorce, but many children in those harder times lost parents to illness or accident. Some lost both, and were raised by grandparents or other relatives. There were orphanages or "homes" for children who had no parents, but those were spoken of in whispers, or used as threats... children died also in those far away times, and one of my earliest memories, and I really must have been very young (no more than 3), was of hearing about a little girl named Patricia, whose mother was a friend of my mother's, who died of asthma.*
>
> *I clearly remember the death of my adored Uncle Georgie, in 1929, when I was 4 years old, of spinal meningitis. (It took me a long time to decode that word – I stored the syllables in my head... and constructed fantasies about them, until, many years later I came across the dreaded word in a book, and made the connection. I did that with a lot of words and concepts – in a family where 'children should be seen and not heard' there is much listening, little questioning, and rich tapestries of fantasy are often woven about unclear words or events)....*

Holding onto the sensibility of her early years, my mother relied on her vivid memories of childhood and family dynamics as she forged connections with the troubled children and families who made up her professional practice. In a story she later wrote for her grandchildren, my mother recreated Uncle Georgie's death, describing the terror she felt at the very thought of "spiny-meany-jitis."

A few days after my grandmother's death, Mom flew to New York for the funeral. There was some confusion about gravesites, in which Uncle Georgie figured prominently: because he had married a divorcee, the Church denied him burial in consecrated ground. His parents (who were also my grandmother's parents) eventually were buried beside him in an unconsecrated section of Flushing Cemetery, despite both their Catholic faith and their disapproval of his marriage. It must have taken great effort and tact for Mom to negotiate with her pious sister and angry brother-in-law about where to inter their mother. Fortunately,

> *...we found an ancient index card in Nana's handwriting indicating that there was still one family grave there in Flushing Cemetery. So, even without a deed, we could reopen Grandpa and Nana's grave and bury Mom with her parents... (for once, my sister and I agreed on something, although I had come to NY determined to be as agreeable and conciliatory as possible, within reason)... We decided against a showing at a funeral home, and a wake, and instead there was just a mass and a graveside service.*
>
> *It was only at the mass that the awful finality of all this really hit me: she is gone and she won't be around any more to worry me or to worry about me, or to love me and be loved by me. Yet, just as I have thought about her, every day of my life thus far, I know that I will continue to think about her daily for the rest of my life... Fathers are important, and God knows my relationship to my father was deep and meaningful to both of us, but I can truly say*

235

that in just about everything I've done in my life, from the most trivial decisions to the most major, the thought 'What would Mom think?' was always present...

So when I found in the back of one her address books a corny, Edgar Guest-ish poem that began 'Do not stand at my grave and weep,/ I am not there, I do not sleep....' I really broke up as I read it, because... she knew that memories are constant, they are always there, everything new that happens associates and links with the past, somehow. And in the fabric of my memories, the threads that connect to Mom are longer, and richer colored, and interweave with more other threads in that pattern than any others.

At the time my mother's mother died, my sister and I were both married, though neither of us was promising babies yet. My parents' first grandchild was born late in 1987, thirty-two years after the birth of their first child and more than two years after Mom poured her heart into this notebook. Nonetheless, in 1985 she had written,

As we get older our memories become more complex and some get lost, or distorted by time. So I'm starting this project, of writing memories down, for my grandchildren, whoever they are – I know that they'll be beautiful, and I know that they'll be warm and sensitive and bright. And I have golden memories that go back a long time, and I want them to have some of them, while I still remember them well, so that the threads in their fabrics will be long and strong.

Even at this early stage, it is easy to see my mother's authorial voice taking shape, anticipating the many stories she would eventually compose for her posterity. Those volumes comprised a particularly grand undertaking, both because of the ambition of the project itself, and because of the assumptions about the future upon which it was founded. In this, my mother's earliest draft, she begins,

> These are the musings of a sixty year old orphan who was born in the 'Roaring Twenties' and who is looking forward to seeing Halley's Comet next year and to the turn of the century – we don't always remember things the same way – my sister's memories are more somber, for the same events that I recall. But then, she was born in 1931 – she was a true Depression Child. I was born in 1925 and I had five full years of the happy, crazy, rich 1920's. I was the only child and the only grandchild – I was doted on, petted, and spoiled rotten by numerous young, unmarried, carefree uncles and aunts. I knew that there was a Depression, and I have many very meaningful Depression memories, but they are laid down on a basically very optimistic, open, trusting base....

Mixed in with these earliest notes for her memoirs, my mother also details the conflict and contention between her and her sister in the days following their mother's death. Apparently, there was some move towards a lawsuit, which Mom did not approve of. In response to her sister's insistence that they hire "a good Christian lawyer," she ranted, "I guess non-Christian lawyers are ambulance chasers... she better not pull anything on me or I'll sick such a Jewish lawyer on her she'll wish she had gotten an Arab crook to represent her! I'm so anxious for all this to be settled so that I can dismiss her from my life."

The next paragraphs reframe one of the keystones of my mother's life story, how her parents met when her mother, a secretary for Pacific Coast Borax in the early '20's offered her father a sample of Boraxo soap to clean his hands. Then Mom digresses into other family tales that came to anchor her early volumes for her grandchildren.

The text peters out after twenty-eight cramped, handwritten pages. If you flip the notebook over, starting on the last page and proceeding backwards, you find early attempts at sketching a table of contents for her reminiscences, interspersed with notes about insurance, bank accounts, doctors' appointments, and trips my parents were planning.

Reading this journal a year and a day after my mother's death, I felt her hand upon me. My whole life I had craved her approval so intensely that I imagined her standing over me, reading and critiquing every word I wrote as it bled to the page; suddenly, *I* was reading over *her* shoulder as she composed the first words of her intended legacy, the collection of stories by which she wanted to be remembered, marking her place with a mass card from her mother's funeral that said, "Pray for us sinners, now and at the hour of our death, Amen."

She had passed the pen to me. It was my turn now to tell our stories.

Yarzheit

In 2008, a few months after my friend Bea's husband took his life, she and I spent a long weekend together in New York. It had been ten years since we'd seen one another, yet the ragged pain of her husband's death drew us back to the easy, sisterly friendship we had shared in our twenties. Hoping to comfort her, I borrowed my sister's apartment on Riverside Drive and invited her to retreat to the scene of a happier, less complicated time in our lives.

Bea was lost in grief that summer. For a few days, as we wept and hugged, we walked all over New York, from Chinatown to Grant's tomb, sentimentally revisiting old haunts, lingering over lattes in upscale coffee shops which had replaced the bookstores that lined upper Broadway in our day, sitting out on the roof with a bottle of wine to watch the sunset over the Hudson. Both conversation and tears flowed freely. And Bea lit candles.

The candles surprised me at first: despite Bea's Catholic upbringing, she is little more connected to organized religion than I am. Walking down Fifth Avenue past St. Patrick's Cathedral, she suddenly tugged me towards the massive doors. "I have to light a candle for my husband," she whispered. The only other time I remembered entering St. Patrick's, I was in elementary school, and what surprised me then was seeing my mother pull out a lace mantilla to drape over her hair; she instructed my sister and me to cover our heads with our handkerchiefs, a detail which, in itself, dates this memory.

I had never before been party to lighting a candle in a church. Bea dropped some coins in the box, genuflected before the tiers of flickering lights, struck a match, and lit a votive. The flame stuttered, then took. Her husband's little red cup glowed among all the others. My friend bowed her head. We both succumbed to tears.

Her husband. He was a lovely, loving man. He was *loved.* His suicide made no sense: even the people who knew him best were blindsided. Can anyone ever truly see into the mind or heart of another?

239

The next morning, after coffee at the Hungarian Pastry Shop on Amsterdam Avenue, Bea led me into the Cathedral of St. John the Divine. Again, she gestured reverently between words and silence, lit a candle, and wept. Above us the vaulted nave rose into high, lonely shadows. No matter who stands beside us in life, I thought, each of us dies alone: Bea's husband died alone, leaving her to stand alone even as I stood beside her facing a dozen rows of tiny flames, each of which embodied the soul of a loved one. And each of which would flicker out in time.

My parents never required their daughters to enter a church or synagogue for any occasion other than weddings, Bar Mitzvahs, funerals, or lessons in art history. They took such pride in being freethinkers that I struggled to find something in their moral universe to reject as I grew up. Sometimes I think this is why I was such a lousy adolescent: if it was simply the right thing to do right, then goddamn it, I would do wrong. I wonder, too, if this is why I remain awestruck by cathedrals, temples, grand and sacred spaces: if they fill a need for others, what need might they fill for me? What have I been missing all my life?

Apart from the menorah at Hanukkah, I had never lit a candle in worship or remembrance, though lighting candles is common to many religious and cultural traditions. Perhaps the first intention was simply to dispel shadows. Ask any child: aren't there valid reasons to fear the dark? It makes sense that this impulse gradually spread to lighting the soul's way into eternal night. The symbolic meaning of light is nearly universal: Light is pure and ineffable. Light illumines. Light negates the oblivion of darkness. Light moves with the speed of... well... *light*, and nothing we know of moves faster. Christians might quote John 8:12, that Christ was "the Light of the world." What I cherish most is the fact that light enables photosynthesis: light, in short, means life.

Not long after Mom died, my sister and I spent an evening reminiscing with our childhood soul mate Kathy, daughter of our mother's best friend. The last time our mothers had seen one another was six summers earlier, on my parents' final visit to Cape

Cod. At the time, we all pretended there would be other reunions, other vacations, but Alzheimer's enforces its cruel limits: that trip was a farewell-tour of the most important friendships of my parents' adult lives.

Kathy and her husband never gave up calling, checking in, visiting my parents a couple of times a year. They redefined family for me. So it felt natural to receive from Kathy's hands a *yarzheit* candle, a candle of remembrance. Jewish custom dictates lighting such a candle at the anniversary of a loved one's death, but we saw no reason to wait. Sitting around the dining room table, welcoming a new year with my sister and my chosen sister, I lit a match. The candle burned as bright as our grief for more than twenty-four hours. It seemed as close to eternity as a little cup of wax could get.

The semester ended two weeks after my mother's death, and I spent much of the winter holidays in bed. It's not that I was ill or depressed: I could have gotten up had I chosen to. But a great wave had broken over my head, its undertow pulling me down into currents that were frightening to swim. Every time I could catch my breath, I thought, "If not now, when?" Let the world keep turning outside my door: I needed time to think through what was mine to accomplish before I walked my mother's path into cognitive decline.

All that came to mind were stories. Her stories. My stories. Stories that had so far kept me company from before my birth into middle age. The way I understood these stories morphed and metamorphosed over time, and I never quite seemed equal to seeing them fledged. Curled under the quilts, I wondered: if I were to pass from this life without finishing more than the slim volumes of poetry I had already produced, what would I leave to the world? It was my job to pick up where my mother left off when Alzheimer's robbed her of her role as keeper of the family narrative. It was my job to embroider the rich threads of the past on the plain linen of the present. To stitch a pattern that would redeem her from forgetting.

241

By shaping her own stories, my mother had hoped to connect her grandchildren to the world of her childhood, in much the same way that her gregarious nature connected my father to the community of their friends. By the time she died, however, Alzheimer's had isolated both my parents so thoroughly from anyone but immediate family that there seemed no point in holding a funeral. This suited my father, who shies from sentiment and ceremony. He even objected when I told him I planned to invite friends in for an open house, an informal memorial to honor Mom. I promised that he did not have to stay, that we would take him home as early as he wanted. He relented. We invited our friends.

Of the people who came to my house three nights after Mom's passing, most had never met my mother. Others had met her once or twice, and remembered her as dimly as she may have remembered them. Only a few had known her well enough to love her.

As it turned out, my father had a wonderful time: he was comforted by their best neighbor at Umbria Court; condoled by our friends who have spent more than a decade nursing a mother whose body has long outlived her mind; reunited with my high school buddy who was always a particular favorite of his; embraced again and again by people upon whom I depend to make the sun come up each morning. There was food, music, and laughter. The guests read passages aloud from *Stories from Grandma,* the giant book Mom had written over a period of ten years for her grandchildren. That evening was a tonic, and a reminder that my mother is still nagging and guiding me, still pushing me to make good.

It wasn't long before I grew tired of lying in bed all day. There is much that I need to do; if not now, when? The only thing I can trust is the fact of finity.

Near the end of Mom's life, my sister loaded an iPod with dozens of songs from the thirties and forties, songs our mother would remember hearing and singing. Sitting in one or another dim institutional room, I'd encourage my mother to recall songs she loved, hoping I could find them on the playlist. Once when I was slow to locate "The Rose of Tralee," her attention wandered; as the first line of the song finally rang in the gloom – "The pale moon was rising above the green mountain" – her hands flew to her throat. "Am I singing?" she cried in alarm.

This is how I discovered *"Bei Mir Bistu Schein,"* Mom's favorite song from her college years. Composed in the '30s for a Yiddish musical, the tune was new to me; my mother, however, wanted to hear it again and again, the way a three year old will clamor for repetitions of a favorite storybook. *"Bei Mir Bistu Schein,"* which means "To Me, You Are Beautiful," became a hit with English lyrics, though it never lost the Yiddish title or refrain. The words are cloying ("I could say *Bella, Bella* / Even say *Wunderbar* / Each language only helps me tell you / How grand you are!"), and Mom was at a loss to keep up with the jaunty rendition on the iPod. Still, in my mind it was the anthem of her final days. It jingled in my head when I couldn't fall asleep, and I'd still be hearing it when I awoke to return to her side, as if my mother's voice kept singing all night inside me. Back at Cascia Hall, after she had largely fallen silent, she still would sit in the Broda chair with her eyes closed and her right hand conducting with an invisible baton, slurring along with the music: *"Bei mir bistu schein* / Again I'll explain / It means you are the fairest in the land...."

The Andrews Sisters, who produced the definitive recording of this song, could not have been more distantly removed from Yiddish culture. Nor could Mom have been at the time she met and fell for my father. Yiddish, in any case, is a mongrel tongue, a catchall vernacular uniquely suited to telling the story of my parents' marriage. *"Bei mir bistu schein,"* my mother sang with some of the last breaths of her life, in some of her final moments of joy. "Each language only helps me tell you how grand you are..."

Yarzheit is a word I have drawn to my heart, though I don't have the patience to wait for anniversaries: every day I feel my mother's influence. Every day she is with me.

So I set wicks to light wherever, whenever I can: lavishly decorated altar candles from *El Rey* Market on Milwaukee's south side; a taper the size of my pinky in the soaring Basilica of Quito; a votive in St. Robert's, a few blocks from my home; second hand stubs planted on homespun altars in Irish holy wells. Each tiny teardrop of flame comforts me as it flickers to life then breaks my heart as it dies. Lacking the words for prayer, I sing to my mother what I will keep singing as long as I have a voice and a memory: *Bei mir bistu schein.*

Notes

The following publications are quoted or referenced in this book:

Books

Augustine, St. *The Confessions.* Translated by Maria Boulding. Hyde Park, NY: New City Press, 2007.

Bishop, Elizabeth. *The Complete Poems, 1927-1979.* New York: Farrar, Strauss and Giroux, 1983.

Cooney, Eleanor. *Death in Slow Motion.* New York: Harper Perennial, 2013.

Driscoll, Eileen. *Alzheimer's: A Handbook For The Caretaker.* Boston: Branden Books, 1994.

Edwards, Caterina. *Finding Rosa.* Vancouver: Greystone Books, 2008.

Gross, Jane. *A Bittersweet Season.* New York: Knopf, 2011.

Harway, Vivian. *Stories From Grandma.* Milwaukee: copyright Vivian Harway, 2007.

Ignatieff, Michael. *Scar Tissue.* New York: Farrar, Strauss and Giroux, 2000.

Pearlman, Mickey. *Listen to Their Voices: Twenty Interviews with Women who Write.* New York: W. W. Norton, 1993.

Schacter, Daniel. *The Seven Sins of Memory.* Boston: Houghton Mifflin Harcourt, 2002.

Thomas, Abigail. *Thinking About Memoir.* Washington, DC: AARP, 2008.

Whitman, Walt. *Leaves of Grass*. New York: Signet Classic, Reprint Edition, 2013.

Whouley, Kate. *Remembering the Music, Forgetting the Words*. Boston: Beacon Press, 2011.

Articles and Websites

Armstrong, Daniel. Personal journal. June, 2011.

Behm, Don. "Ex-CEO McNeer Accused of Trying to Kill Wife." *Milwaukee Journal-Sentinel*, 12/7/2011. http://www.jsonline.com/news/ozwash/125183073.html

Belluck, Pam. "Giving Alzheimer's Patients Their Way, Even Chocolate." *The New York Times*, 12/31/2010. http://www.nytimes.com/2011/01/01/health/01care.html

Boulton, Guy. "Medical Field Looks to Comfort the Ill." *Milwaukee Journal-Sentinel*, 10/31/2011. http://www.jsonline.com/features/health/medical-field-looks-to-comfort-the-ill-132941128.html

Columbia-St. Mary's Hospital. *Physician Directory*. www.columbia-stmary's.org/ (10/8/2011)

Featherly, Kevin. "Legendary Wrestler Verne Gagne and a Tragic Tale." *MinnPost*, 2/18/2009. http://www.minnpost.com/politics-policy/2009/02/legendary-wrestler-verne-gagne-and-tragic-tale

Glauber, Bill. "'Nobody Wants Our Dad:' 3 Daughters Battle Health System, Legal Maze as Father Fights Alzheimer's." *Milwaukee Journal Sentinel*, 3/10/2010. http://www.jsonline.com/features/health/87185282.html

Glauber, Bill. "Father Caught in Legal Morass Dies of Pneumonia." *Milwaukee Journal-Sentinel,* 3/10/2010. http://www.jsonline.com/news/milwaukee/87301092.html

Glauber, Bill. "Nursing Home Calls to Police Hint at Dilemma of Dementia." *Milwaukee Journal-Sentinel,* 12/7/2010. http://www.jsonline.com/features/health/111504319.html

Glauber, Bill. "Alzheimer's Task Force Calls for Overhaul." *Milwaukee Journal-Sentinel,* 12/14/2010. http://www.jsonline.com/features/health/111834364.html

Harway, Vivian. Personal journal. July, 1985.

Hippocrates and Lasagna, Louis. "The Hippocratic Oath." http://www.pbs.org/wgbh/nova/body/hippocratic-oath-today.html

Kubler-Ross, Elisabeth. http://www.ekrfoundation.org

Resnick, Jack. "Bring Healthcare Home." *The New York Times,* 12/4/2011. http://www.nytimes.com/2011/12/05/opinion/bring-health-care-home.html

Seligson, Susan. "Be Gentle. I Know My Dog is Old." *The Bark Magazine.* Issue 63: Feb/March 2011.

About the Author

Judith Harway's books of poetry include *All That is Left* (2009), a finalist for the Eric Hoffer Award, and two chapbooks, *Swimming in the Sky* (2014) and *The Memory Box* (2002). She is Professor of Writing and Humanities at the Milwaukee Institute of Art and Design, a two-time recipient of the Wisconsin Arts Board literature fellowship, and a widely published poet and essayist. She and her husband, musician Dan Armstrong, make their home in the Milwaukee area, with three rescued dogs who have happily replaced their grown children.

Made in the USA
Lexington, KY
17 September 2015